seriously
dating ^or
engaged

seriously dating or engaged

a premarital workbook for couples

DR. ROGER TIRABASSI MA, DMIN

with Becky Tirabassi

BECKY
TIRABASSI
change your life®

Newport Beach, California

BECKY
TIRABASSI
change your life®

Newport Beach, California
Printed in the USA

Seriously Dating or Engaged: A Premarital Workbook
Copyright © 2009 by Roger Tirabassi, D Min., MA, Becky Tirabassi

Includes bibliographical references and index.
   ISBN# 978-0-9825388-0-7

a word about mentor couples...

Many of you will go through the material in this Workbook with a counselor or pastor. Other couples will be a part of a premarital class.

For those couples going through *Seriously Dating or Engaged* on your own, please consider asking a married couple to walk alongside of you through each chapter. If you attend a local church, ask if they have a mentor program or if the staff is willing to help you find a mentor couple. If they are not able to help you, ask a couple that you feel has a good marriage to work through the material with you. (*A Leader's Guide immediately follows the last chapter of the Workbook.*)

If a mentor couple does go through the Workbook with you, meet every week (or every other week) until you complete all eight chapters. After you marry, it is equally important to meet with your mentor couple at least four times a year for the first two years of your marriage.

What is the role of a mentor couple before marriage?

Mentor couples can answer questions you might encounter when going through the material. They can review your assignments and reflections from each chapter as well as help you locate recommended resources or contact a pastor for additional support. Finally, if trained, they can take you through the recommended PREPARE Inventory.

What is the role of a mentor couple after marriage?

After marriage, it is very common for newlyweds to encounter problems. A mentor couple can support and encourage you, answer questions during your adjustment stages, and help you stay accountable to your worksheets and systems. Mentor couples can also assist you in finding marriage enrichment experiences or other resources that will help you grow stronger in your marriage.

table of contents

Chapter Six: Sexual Intimacy

Chapter Seven: Parenting

Chapter Eight: Next Steps

ADDENDUMS:

introduction

When Becky and I speak to seriously dating and engaged couples, we often use the analogy of working with people on drugs. Natural chemicals such as dopamine, endorphins, serotonin, and oxytocin can cause the same reaction as a drug. Dating and engaged couples often find themselves in this chemically induced condition. They have an uncanny ability to focus on their partner's positive strengths and traits, rarely noticing the reality of their partner's weaknesses. Our sincere hope is that by the time you finish *Seriously Dating or Engaged*, you will get "off drugs" and see your partner, your relationship, and eventually your marriage in a more realistic and less idealistic way.

While on the subject of reality…

By going through our workbook, some of you will determine that now is not the right time to move forward in your relationship or that you are not in the right relationship. This is not uncommon. The Prepare/Enrich premarital program suggests that about 15-20% of couples going through a premarital class will cancel their wedding plans and should not get married (www.prepare-enrich.com). If you discover this about your relationship, we encourage you to take careful steps toward reevaluating your relationship or at least delaying your wedding. The immediate pain you experience in breaking up now or by delaying your wedding will save you much greater heartache in the future.

Realistically, marriage takes a great deal of work. We often tell our couples, "You will either do premarital education or post-marital counseling. Besides, premarital training is a lot more fun and a lot less expensive." In fact, according to research, couples that received pre-marital education lower their chance of divorce by thirty-one percent.[1]

Before proceeding, it is important to acknowledge that over the past few decades, the way our culture views marriage has significantly changed. But Becky and I firmly believe that God's viewpoint of marriage hasn't changed—it is a life-long commitment. Therefore, *Seriously Dating or Engaged* is not only written from a biblical perspective, but it strategically includes comprehensive and practical worksheets to help you successfully merge your unique personalities (with different family of origins and financial habits) into one new union.

Finally, the material in *Seriously Dating or Engaged* has been developed over many years and used by hundreds of couples in my private counseling practice and our premarital classes. Though Becky and I have written this workbook together, we've determined that I will be the one to guide you through it. Whether you go through the material (1) in four or eight weeks, (2) on your own as a couple, (3) with a mentor/counselor/pastor, or (4) as part of a class, we are confident that *Seriously Dating or Engaged* will prepare you for marriage by providing you with the necessary knowledge, skills, and decisions for making your relationship safe and satisfying.

Let's get started…

---

1 Jayson, Sharon. *Premarital Education Could Cut Divorce Rate*, June 22, 2006, <u>USA Today</u>

 1

communicating effectively

A national survey of more than forty thousand married couples found that communication was the most important factor in distinguishing happy couples from unhappy couples.[1] That is why we begin *Seriously Dating or Engaged* by teaching couples foundational skills and systems for effective communication—how to listen, how to respond, and how to share their thoughts and feelings with each other.

Good communication is the foundation of good relationships. It increases intimacy, helps resolve conflicts and enhances an overall satisfaction in relationships. Poor communication increases defensiveness, creates barriers to resolving conflicts and eventually leads to a loss of intimacy. Therefore it is critical that couples learn effective communication skills that protect them from the dangers associated with poor communication.

We begin with **15 Rules for Effective Communication**…

 15 Rules for Effective Communication

1. We won't use the words "NEVER" or "ALWAYS."
2. We won't blame or shame.
3. We won't name call, label or belittle.
4. We won't use "You statements."
5. We won't tell the other person we are "angry" at them.
6. We won't lose control.
7. We won't withdraw or isolate.
8. We won't speak until we have completely listened to our partner.
9. We won't make demands.
10. We won't use threats.
11. We won't criticize.
12. We won't interrupt.
13. We won't use the "D" or "divorce" word.
14. We won't use generalizations.
15. We won't tell the other person they broke a rule.

The 15 Rules in Detail:

1   We won't use the words "NEVER" or "ALWAYS."

Using words such as *always, never, nothing,* and *every* can complicate communication and create defensive reactions. In addition, phrases such as, "You are always late," "You never pay attention," "You never listen," or "You are always watching sports," can cause your partner to get defensive. When you or your partner gets defensive, an escalation into deeper problems can occur. In order to avoid escalating and defensiveness, only discuss the specific incident that occurred. For example, if your partner was late today and this irritated you, you might say, "When you were late this morning, it made me feel as if you didn't care about me or that I am not important to you." It may be the umpteenth time he or she was late, but the secret of effective communication is discussing only the *current* incident. This first rule is a foundation for minimizing defensiveness.

2   We won't blame or shame.

Many arguments worsen because we fall into the *blame* or *shame* game. In order to avoid blaming your partner, completely eliminate certain phrases such as, "If it wasn't for you…" or "You started this," or "This is your fault," or "You are like your mother." To avoid shaming your partner, eliminate the phrase, "You're wrong." Instead, express how you are experiencing the incident. Rather than trying to win a point or prove who is right and who is wrong, just share how you perceived the situation. For example, you might say, "That is how I experienced the situation," rather than saying, "I'm right," or "You are wrong." By acknowledging that you experience things differently, you minimize the risk of escalating into an argument.

3   We won't name call, label or belittle.

The old adage, "sticks and stones may break my bones, but names will never hurt me," does not take into consideration the negative effect words can have on us. Words can do substantial damage to a relationship. Labeling your partner as *lazy, selfish, controlling, critical,* or *manipulative* will only create more difficulties for your relationship.

4   We won't use "You" statements.

We'll use "*I feel*" statements instead. "*You*" statements create defensiveness. "I feel" statements make it easier for your partner to accept your feelings. For example, instead of saying "You are not listening to me," say "I feel that I am not being heard."

5   We won't tell the other person we are "angry" at them.

Anger is a secondary emotion. It proceeds from other primary emotions like hurt, irritation, frustration, abandonment or rejection. To communicate effectively with each other, it is important to identify your root feelings that came before your anger and express those instead. (See the list of feelings/emotions later in this chapter). Anger often evokes tension. Instead, expressing "hurt" feelings will evoke compassion. Most importantly, your partner is likely to be less defensive if you say, "I am hurt," or "I am irritated," rather than "I am angry." James 1:19 says, "My dear brothers, take note of this: Everyone should be quick to listen, slow to speak and slow to become angry."

6 We won't lose control.

Take a "time-out" if you or your partner become angry to the point of being out-of-control. Losing control is a very dangerous behavior within any relationship. Couples often have a very difficult time healing from statements or accusations that their partner or parents have said to them in anger. Taking a "time-out" (see Chapter Four) becomes a very important and effective communication skill to use when your feelings begin to escalate. Proverbs 29:11 states, "A fool gives full vent to his anger, but a wise man keeps himself under control."

7 We won't withdraw or isolate.

Withdrawing or isolating can be as harmful as outbursts of anger. These behaviors create powerful experiences of abandonment and rejection. Taking a mutually agreed upon "time-out" (for a specific amount of time) can help you or your partner gain self control, but just walking away can cause deep pain. Agree upon a memorized statement that either of you will use to signal that you need a "time-out." For example, when Becky and I begin to escalate in a conversation, we say the following statement, "I love you and you love me and we don't want to do this." This statement causes us to pause. Then we are able to take a personal "time-out" without causing the other person to feel abandoned. The goal of a "time-out" is not withdrawal or isolation, but to get control of your emotions and resume discussion with your partner as soon as possible. Proverbs 18:1 NAS reminds us that, "He who separates himself seeks his own desire. He quarrels against all sound wisdom."

8 We won't speak until we have completely listened to our partner.

Listening is one of the most important aspects of effective communication because it is integral to resolving conflicts and developing intimacy. Therefore it is important to take painstaking steps to hear everything your partner has to say. As you proceed through this workbook, you'll be instructed in how to become both an *intentional* and *empathetic* listener. Though intentional, empathetic listening can be very difficult, over time it will enhance your relationship. Proverbs 18:13 says, "He who answers before listening—that is his folly and shame."

9 We won't make demands.

When couples are in the *infatuation* stage they are usually very polite and not very demanding of each other. However, soon after the honeymoon, they begin to treat each other differently. Their requests often sound more like demands. It is very easy for married couples to fall into the habit of telling their partner what to do rather than asking for help unless they determine in advance to communicate politely. Asking, rather than demanding, is an important rule of effective communication because it protects your relationship.

10 We won't use threats.

When you hear the "*if*" word, it can often signal that a threatening statement will follow. For example, when you hear or say, "*If* you don't stop this…" or "*If* you continue to do this…" you are heading into dangerous communication territory. Though you might not feel as if you are threatening your partner when we use the "*if*" word, they might feel threatened. Therefore, it is important to acknowledge that the "*if*" word can be used as a threat. In fact, many of you have been raised by parents who used the "*if*" word in this way, and it is likely that you will either be prone to use it or have an adverse reaction when you hear it. Threats cause recurring frustrations and irritations between couples, therefore it is critical to understand and adhere to this rule.

11 *We won't criticize.*

Criticism kills intimacy. Affirmation builds love. Therefore, it is important to affirm your partner *before* you attempt to share your frustrations or irritations with them. As a counselor, I repeatedly see couples that have allowed criticism to become a normal communication pattern in their relationship. It's not long before they regularly hurt each other, resulting in loss of intimacy. When I ask a couple who is caught in this cycle to stop *all* criticism for one entire week, they report back that their relationship significantly improved. On those occasions when you want your partner to know that they have hurt, frustrated, or irritated you, it is imperative that you begin your discussion by affirming them. Be sure your affirmation is authentic, specific and includes supporting evidence. For example, you might say to your partner who is late because they were out with a good friend, "I appreciate how caring you are toward your friends. In fact, I love that about you. However, I felt frustrated tonight when you came home 30 minutes late for dinner." Beginning with affirmations removes defensiveness and allows you to converse more calmly and safely with your partner.

12 *We won't interrupt.*

In any conversation, it is rude to interrupt. That doesn't mean there won't be times when your partner is talking and you will be tempted to correct a fact or make a counterpoint. At this juncture, use self-control. Rather than interrupt, wait until your partner is done speaking. Then repeat back to them what you heard them saying. This is not to correct a fact or to disagree, but to confirm that you have heard them correctly. Throughout the workbook, you will be given additional skills for mirroring, listening and conflict resolution. The goal of effective communication is for both partners to safely share their thoughts and feelings with each other.

13 *We won't use the "D" or "divorce" word.*

Before Becky and I were married, we made a commitment that no matter what happened, we would never use the word "divorce." Over thirty-one years later, we have never used the word in our communication with each other. This has given us complete security in our marriage as divorce *has never* and *will never* be an option. Why is this a non-negotiable rule? When a person talks about divorce in a threatening manner, they are causing considerable damage to their relationship. The use of the word "divorce" breeds insecurity and causes feelings of abandonment, fear, and hopelessness. Because it can be so damaging, I suggest that dating and engaged couples commit to adhering to a similar rule. For example, equivalent threats for those who are dating would be phrases such as, "Maybe we should end this now," or "Maybe we aren't good for each other," or "Maybe we should just break-up." It is very easy for dating or engaged couples, when they are irritated or frustrated, to use similar phrases to the "D" word. This harmful habit will turn into an unhealthy pattern. (Note: Not all dating or engaged couples *will* or *should* get married. Therefore, during the premarital stage, if you feel that you should not continue in a serious relationship, it is best to carefully handle "break-up" conversations in the presence of a counselor or pastor or mentor couple. In dating or marriage, it is important not to use "relationship-terminating" phrases in the heat of an argument or when you are upset.)

14 *We won't use generalizations.*

Making general statements about someone is a very common and hurtful communication mistake. The most important reason to avoid using generalizations is because they cause defensive reactions, rather than create resolution. In many cases, recurring behaviors build up over time and instead of dealing with a specific incident, the temptation is to accuse your partner of overall poor behavior or character. Instead of generalizing, express how you felt as a result of a specific behavior or incident. An example of a generalization would be, "I don't feel that you love me." A specific statement would be, "I didn't feel loved when you forgot our anniversary."

15 *We won't tell the other person they broke a rule.*

These rules are guidelines for you. They should not be used as accusations but to help both of you become more effective communicators. Once you decide to abide by these rules, you will most likely be tempted to tell your partner that they broke a rule. If your partner breaks a rule, instead of telling them they broke the "*never and always*" rule say, "I felt frustrated or hurt when you said that I *always*…" Just remember, if you tell your partner "You just broke a rule," *you* are actually breaking two rules: Fourteen and Fifteen!

 Couple Assignment

Discuss each rule. Talk about what you will do when you are tempted to break that rule and what you will do if your partner breaks that rule. (For suggestions, see Rule 15.)

If you are willing to practice these guidelines in your relationship, sign and date the following agreement. Remember, with time and practice and patience, these rules will improve your communication skills.

 Individual Reflection

Determine which rule you think (or know) will be most difficult for you to follow. Which rule does your partner break that is most frustrating to you? How can you avoid becoming defensive when he or she breaks this rule?

15 Rules for Effective Communication Agreement

We won't use the words "NEVER" or "ALWAYS."

We won't blame or shame.

We won't name call, label or belittle.

We won't use "You statements."

We won't tell the other person we are "angry" at them.

We won't lose control.

We won't withdraw or isolate.

We won't speak until we have completely listened to our partner.

We won't make demands.

We won't use threats.

We won't criticize.

We won't interrupt.

We won't use the "D" or "divorce" word.

We won't use generalizations.

We won't tell the other person they broke a rule.

*In our relationship, I agree to abide by these rules to the best of my ability.
When I break a rule, I will admit it and ask for forgiveness.*

_____   _____
Name   Date   Name   Date

Couple Assignment

Communication between couples improves when you accurately identify your feelings, but it is even more helpful to communicate the intensity of your feelings.

Choose one word from each list below (positive/negative). Then share a time when you experienced that feeling as well as the intensity of the feeling. Why did you feel the way you did?

Intensity of Feelings: *Rate intensity on a scale of 1-10 (1 is mild, 5 is moderate, 10 is strong.)*

Words to Identify Your Feelings

Positive or Happy Feelings:

Happy	Overjoyed	Glorious	Affectionate
Secure	Controlled	Joyful	Amazed
Passionate	Calm	Surprised	Comforted
Generous	Relieved	Loved	Comfortable
Silly	Competent	Peaceful	Supported
Excited	Friendly	Optimistic	Youthful
Liked	Comforted	Understood	Satisfied
Relaxed	Hopeful	Connected	Infatuated
Soft	Fantastic	Accepted	Forgiven
Committed	Compassionate	Pleased	Competent

Negative or Painful Feelings:

Irritated	Hurt	Suspicious	Frustrated
Awkward	Abandoned	Sad	Fear/Fearful
Proud	Humiliated	Pressured	Confused
Torn	Cut off	Uncertain	Defeated
Unsure	Deprived	Useless	Disappointed
Worthless	Dominated	Unappreciated	Embarrassed
Ignored	Insecure	Impatient	Misunderstood
Disrespected	Apprehensive	Shocked	Immobilized
Guilty	Demeaned	Lonely	Depressed
Jealous	Helpless	Hopeless	Disconnected
Rejected	Ugly		

How comfortable are you when sharing your feelings with your partner (on a scale of 1-10?) Are you seeing any improvement with identifying your feelings as well as your partner's feelings? Explain.

INTENTIONAL-EMPATHETIC LISTENING

Proverbs 18:13 suggests that, "He who answers before listening—that is his folly and shame."

Listening does not come naturally for most of us. Therefore, numerous wise counselors have been teaching people how to listen to each other for decades. In 1975, Thomas Gordon, author of **Parent Effectiveness Training**, created a listening system called *active listening*. More recently, relationship expert Harville Hendrix designed a listening system called the *Imago Dialogue*. Howard Markman's book, **Fighting For Your Marriage**, calls his system the *Speaker-Listener Technique*.

As a counselor and pastor, I realize how important it is for couples to have a practical system for both talking and listening to each other when they disagree, feel misunderstood or are hurt by each other. Because of this, I've developed an *Intentional-Empathetic Listening* system that helps couples to intentionally incorporate empathy into their listening patterns.

Empathy is the ability to understand another person by identifying with his or her feelings. Most importantly, it is a skill that can be learned. Empathy begins with listening, then identifying another's feelings, as well as acknowledging the intensity of his or her feelings. It also includes recalling a time in your life in which you experienced the same feeling(s).

I teach all of my premarital and married couples the following 10 Steps to *Intentional-Empathetic Listening:*

 10 Steps to Intentional-Empathetic Listening

1. Decide who will be the *Listener* and who will be the *Talker*.
2. The *Talker* begins with affirmations that are specific to the situation.
3. The *Talker* shares his or her thoughts and feelings by using "I feel" statements.
4. The *Listener* repeats what the *Talker* said and asks if they got it correct.
5. The *Listener* empathizes.
6. The *Listener* apologizes and asks for forgiveness.

7. The *Listener* asks the *Talker* if there is anything more he or she wants to share regarding this specific incident.

8. The *Talker*, if necessary, shares more "I feel" statements.

9. The *Listener* repeats the *Talker's* feelings and thoughts, and then asks if he or she understood correctly. If not, the *Listener* will repeat the empathizing response (Step 5).

10. Reverse Roles. The *Talker* now becomes the *Listener* and starts with Step 2.

The 10 Steps to Intentional-Empathetic Listening in Detail:

1   Decide who will be the Listener *and who will be the* Talker.

Many couples get into trouble at the beginning of an intense conversation because they both want to talk! In such cases, as soon as possible, designate one partner to talk first. They are called the *Talker*. (Sometimes it is even helpful for the *Talker* to hold an object (like a water bottle or a pen) to mimic a microphone. Using a "prop" eliminates any confusion as to who is the *Talker* and who is the *Listener*.)

2   The Talker *begins by sharing something they appreciate or love about their partner. It should relate to the topic they are going to address.*

The second step in the *Intentional-Empathetic Listening* system is for the Talker to begin by sharing an affirmation with their partner. This is an essential step so don't skip it. It is especially important because negative feelings such as frustration, irritation, or hurt that can cause defensiveness will also be communicated during this time. However, if you begin the conversation by affirming your partner, you minimize the chances of a defensive reaction.

For example, if Becky was hurt when I came home late from work, we would designate her as the *Talker*. Before telling me that she did not feel that I cared for her, she would begin by telling me that she appreciated when I made us dinner the night before (and did the dishes, as well). She would express affirmation for those actions that made her feel that I was caring for her. It is often necessary to share two or three affirmations to offset a defensive reaction. Research shows it can take up to five positive interactions to equal one negative comment, so the more affirmations the better.[2] I consider this affirmation process similar to giving a patient anesthesia before surgery. Imagine a dentist or doctor neglecting to give you a shot of anesthesia before an operation. We would never think of having surgery without anesthesia, so we should not proceed with emotional surgery without providing a pain minimizer.

3   The Talker *shares his or her thoughts and feelings using "I feel" statements.*

In this step, it is important to avoid referring to the past, by saying "You always do this..." The *Talker* must do their best to follow the *15 Rules for Effective Communication*, with the goal of communicating your feelings about a specific incident, while at the same time minimizing your partner's defensive reactions. At this juncture, if either partner moves into destructive anger, it is important to take a time-out and/or use the Anger Management/Time-out

Worksheet in Chapter Four. Accurately identifying your feelings is necessary for *Intentional-Empathetic Listening* to be effective. Please use the list of feeling words, and if necessary, keep them in front of you during this step until you become more skilled at identifying them.

4 *The* Listener *repeats what the* Talker *said, being sure to accurately repeat the* Talker's *thoughts and feelings.*

The *Listener* carefully repeats what they heard the *Talker* say. For example, they might respond, "You said that you really appreciate how I do the laundry and how this makes you feel supported. But you didn't feel supported when I forgot to put my dirty socks in the laundry basket again this morning." This step often feels a bit mechanical, but if you skip it, you can't be sure you that you have understood your partner. Before you can move to the next step, the *Talker* must feel understood by the *Listener*. (If you ever played the childhood game of "Telephone," in which one person whispers something in one person's ear and it gets passed along, you know how important it is for the *Talker* and *Listener* to communicate accurately.)

In order to prevent miscommunication, after the *Listener* repeats what they heard, they must ask the question, "Did I hear you correctly?" Harville Hendrix even encourages couples to ask, "Is there anything more?" This allows the *Talker* to express any additional feelings that occurred during the incident being discussed.

5 *The* Listener *Empathizes.*

In this step, the *Listener* recalls an experience when he or she had the same feeling that the *Talker* is expressing. This allows the *Listener* to feel what the *Talker* is feeling, becoming empathetic toward his or her partner. The key to empathy is identifying with your partner's feelings, so that you can recall a time in your life when you had that exact feeling.

For example, if your partner didn't feel supported when you forgot to put your laundry in the hamper, you would think of a time when you didn't feel supported, rather than recall when someone was inconsiderate or forgetful. So you might say, "I think I know what you are feeling because I did not feel supported by my coworker when he didn't finish his part of the project we had to complete recently. Is that correct?" It is important NOT to use an example that includes your partner.

It would be inappropriate to say, "I think I know how you are feeling because when you drove my car last night you forgot to close the sun roof and dew got on the seats."

Intentional-Empathetic Listening takes practice. It is important in Step 5 for the *Listener* to empathize with the *Talker* by identifying exact feelings, but not turning the focus of the discussion toward the *Listener*. The empathetic response should be brief, but significant enough for the *Listener* to feel what the *Talker* is feeling, in order to convey understanding. When couples master *Intentional-Empathetic Listening* their relationship is able to achieve a higher level of intimacy.

6 *The* Listener *apologizes and asks for forgiveness.*

If you have hurt your partner deeply, this process will take time, depending on the level of pain. However, the goal of this step is for the *Listener* to ask forgiveness for hurting his or her partner. For example, the *Listener* might say, "I'm so sorry for hurting you and causing you to feel that I didn't care about you. Will you forgive me?" An inappropriate statement would be, "I am sorry you felt that way." This step requires humility. Therefore it is most important for the *Listener* to specifically ask the *Talker* for forgiveness, completing the transaction.

It is important to acknowledge that forgiveness doesn't immediately eliminate all the hurt nor does it relieve all the responsibility for the pain. In time, however, if you both work through this process, you should experience both forgiveness and healing. If you need to further discuss the specific issue in greater detail, follow the *8 Step Process for Resolving Conflict* in Chapter Four.

7 *The* Listener *asks the* Talker *if there is anything more he or she wants to share regarding this specific incident.*

The *Listener* asks, "Is there anything more you want to share with me about this incident?" The purpose of this step is to allow the *Talker* to feel as if they have had an adequate opportunity to share their thoughts and feelings regarding this incident without interruption or anger.

8 *The* Talker, *if necessary, shares more "I feel" statements.*

In response to the invitation to share anything more, the *Talker* must be careful not to include additional incidents in this discussion. They can share additional thoughts or feelings regarding the specific incident.

9 *The* Listener *repeats the* Talker's *feelings and thoughts, and then asks if he or she has understood correctly.*

If there is more, the *Listener* will repeat with empathizing responses (Step 5). This process continues until the *Talker* feels as if the *Listener* accurately understands his or her feelings regarding this incident.

10 *Reverse Roles.*

The *Talker* now becomes *Listener* and starts with Step 2. It is very important that both partners have an equal chance to completely express his or her feelings without anger, interruption, or defensiveness. Use a hand signal to identify when your partner breaks a rule or gives too much information, such as placing your hand on your chest. Rather than interrupting, this gives the *Talker* an opportunity to self-correct or the *Listener* an opportunity to repeat what they heard.

Intentional-Empathetic Listening allows couples to enter into a deeper level of intimacy by experiencing connectedness, love, compassion and healing. Initially this exercise feels mechanical to everyone. However, most new activities feel unnatural in the beginning. As with all new habits, expect that it will take time to feel comfortable with this system. Be patient with each other.

Couple Assignment

Set aside twenty minutes to practice the *Intentional-Empathetic Listening* system by sharing a positive experience in which your partner did something to make you feel loved, secure, or encouraged. Begin with *Step 1* and decide who will be the *Listener* and who will be the *Talker*. Before you begin, review the list of "Feeling" words to help you accurately express your emotions and read the following example. For this exercise, only use positive statements or affirmations. No negative comments at this point!

Talker: *I want to thank you for taking care of me after my knee surgery. You picked up my medications and got up at two o'clock in the morning to get my ice packs. I really appreciated how you took care of me; it made me feel safe. Thank you.*

Listener: *What you are trying to tell me is that you felt safe and cared for by me when I went to get your medication and got up in the middle of the night to get you ice. Is there anything else you want to add to that?*

Talker: *No.*

Listener: *I remember a time I felt that way. When I broke my ankle, my mom took care of me by standing in line to get my medication and making my meals. I felt loved and safe. Have I described your feeling accurately?*

Listener: *Yes!*

Reverse roles.

Individual Reflection

Record how you felt during the *Intentional-Empathetic Listening* exercise. Were you comfortable or hesitant to share your feelings? What was the most difficult aspect of the exchange for you? What was your partner's reaction to this exercise?

10 Steps to Intentional-Empathetic Listening Worksheet

1. Decide who will be the *Listener* and who will be the *Talker*.
2. The *Talker* begins with affirmations that are specific to the situation.
3. The *Talker* shares his or her thoughts and feelings by using "I feel" statements.
4. The *Listener* repeats what the *Talker* said and asks if they got it correct.
5. The *Listener* empathizes.
6. The *Listener* apologizes and asks for forgiveness.
7. The *Listener* asks the *Talker* if there is anything more he or she wants to share regarding this specific incident.
8. The *Talker*, if necessary, shares more "I feel" statements.
9. The *Listener* repeats the *Talker's* feelings and thoughts, and then asks if he or she understood correctly. If not, the *Listener* will repeat the empathizing response (Step 5).
10. Reverse Roles. The *Talker* now becomes the *Listener* and starts with Step 2.

THE DAILY 5 A'S

Couples often struggle in their relationship shortly after marriage. As a counselor, I discover that they treated each other more courteously before and during the honeymoon. After marriage, they realize that they must become more intentional with their responses. Believe it or not, I have to remind married couples to affirm each other more, be more affectionate with each other, apologize more quickly, ask for help if they need it, and offer to pray for each other daily. I call this system the *Daily 5 A's*.

I have been using and teaching the *Daily 5 A's* for almost fifteen years, even including them in my wedding ceremonies. This simple, three-to-five minute activity is an intentional exercise, if regularly practiced, will help couples grow in intimacy. Couples can take turns sharing one "A" at a time or completing all *Daily 5 A's* at once. It depends upon your personal preference.

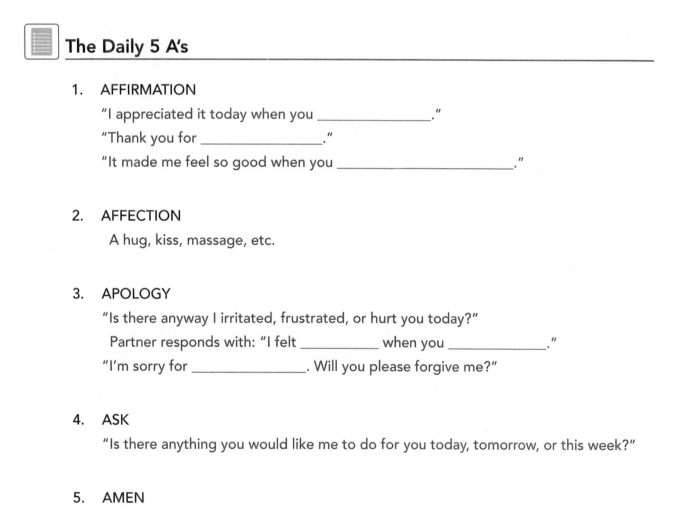

The Daily 5 A's

1. **AFFIRMATION**
    "I appreciated it today when you _____."
    "Thank you for _____."
    "It made me feel so good when you _____."

2. **AFFECTION**
    A hug, kiss, massage, etc.

3. **APOLOGY**
    "Is there anyway I irritated, frustrated, or hurt you today?"
    Partner responds with: "I felt _____ when you _____."
    "I'm sorry for _____. Will you please forgive me?"

4. **ASK**
    "Is there anything you would like me to do for you today, tomorrow, or this week?"

5. **AMEN**
    "How can I specifically pray for you today?"
    Close your time with a short prayer.

The 5 A's in Detail

Affirmation

John Gottman, PhD, a world-renowned researcher on marriage is convinced that for survival, couples need five positive interactions for every one negative interaction.[3] Another marriage expert, Willard Harley, believes that each relationship is like a bank that, in order, to stay healthy needs more deposits than withdrawals.[4] Affirmation is absolutely essential for healthy relationships.

The first *Daily A* is *affirmation*. Though affirming your partner should be simple, some couples actually find it difficult to affirm each other on a daily basis. They express concern that their affirmation might sound shallow or insincere; but with very little effort most couples can overcome those types of barriers very quickly.

Here are a few examples of positive affirmations:

- "I appreciated it so much when you brought flowers to me today. It made me feel so loved."
- "Thank you for reminding me that my driver's license was about to expire. I almost forgot. It made me feel like you were watching out for me."
- "Thanks for making the final arrangements for our honeymoon today. I am really looking forward to our time together."
- "You looked so nice tonight at dinner. I find myself so attracted to you!"
- "I liked the way you talked to the waiter today. You're so respectful of others. I admire that so much about you."

Be sure to avoid making slightly negative comments during your affirmation, such as, "I was surprised when you helped with the dishes tonight because last week you complained so much about helping me."

Affection

The second *Daily A* is *affection*. Touch is a critical component to healthy emotional development. In fact, Gary Chapman, author of **Five Love Languages**, considers physical touch as one of the primary ways a person experiences love. Therefore, the purpose of this *Daily A* is simply to hold hands, cuddle, share a little kiss or give your partner a short back rub. Even if your partner is out of town, you can "smooch" him or her over the phone so they can hear it. Especially when you're tired or busy, it is important to intentionally take the time to be affectionate with each other.

Apology

I am convinced that if the majority of struggling couples had willingly and humbly developed the habit of apologizing to each other on a daily basis, they might not have needed counseling. Keeping "short accounts" with each other and regularly asking for forgiveness cannot be over-emphasized.

Why? Hurting each other is unavoidable. The more time couples spend together, the more opportunities they have to hurt one another. The habit of making daily apologies is essential to maintaining a healthy and intimate relationship.

Seldom does anyone hurt his or her partner purposely. On occasion though, we *all* hurt those we love. Overanalyzing the third *Daily A* of apology will overshadow what really matters—improving intimacy. (Of course, if you've hurt your partner more deeply, this process will not be sufficient. In those cases, the *Intentional-Empathetic Listening* system should be employed. I do not recommend processing deep hurt while using the *Daily 5 A's*. Instead, schedule another time to process this level of hurt.)

On a daily basis, the best way I have found to share this *Daily A* is by asking the following question, "Is there any way I have irritated, frustrated, or hurt you?" After your partner responds with one, and only one, incident in which he or she has been irritated, frustrated or hurt, it is imperative that the person who asked the question responds with, "I am sorry for irritating you. Will you forgive me?"

Finally, to ensure success in this exercise, resist defending yourself when it is your partner's turn to share if he or she has been hurt.

> Example: When I recently asked Becky if there was any way I hurt, irritated or frustrated her, I expected her to say, "No, I can't think of anything." Instead, she said, "Actually there is something. It irritated me when you came home in a bad mood from work and let that filter into our evening." My first thought was, "I did not come home in a bad mood." But instead I responded with, "I am sorry for irritating you. Will you forgive me?" Though I didn't feel as if I had come home in a bad mood, Becky experienced it differently. If my actions and attitude caused her to feel this way, they weren't worth defending. The next day, when I got home, I gave her a big kiss and said, "Hi honey! How are you? Give me a big hug." Over the many years of doing the *Daily 5 A's*, being intentional with each other has given us a very fun and safe relationship. We regularly experience the long-term benefits of apologizing quickly and avoiding minor conflicts.

Ask

The fourth *Daily A* is designed to give you an opportunity to daily serve your partner. Simply ask your partner, "Is there anything I can do for you today?" This is not meant to be a long list of chores. Your request should be limited to one item per day. Some examples include:

"Would you mind taking the trash out for me tomorrow?"
"Would you be willing to put gas in my car?"
"Would you be willing to make reservations for us to go to the play?"
"Would you be willing to go to the bookstore for me this week?"

The fourth *Daily A* is intended to help you assist your partner in a simple, helpful manner. If you have a longer list of things that must get done, schedule a separate time for having a different conversation to accomplish those tasks. Please keep in mind that you are "asking," not "demanding."

Amen

The fifth *Daily A* is a special time to ask, "How can I pray for you right now?" This is a short prayer time, not intended to be a prayer meeting or a discussion. It is designed to be a brief time of spiritually caring for each other. If you are not comfortable praying out loud, this will be a new experience. But all my couples report that this *Daily A* has significantly deepened their level of intimacy. Examples of prayer requests include: God's hand upon the details of an important, upcoming meeting, the plans to fall together on a project, a deadline to be met, a particular concern that weighs heavily on your heart.

Example: Many times Becky asks me to pray for an upcoming speaking engagement. She really enjoys when I pray, "Lord, please help Becky to hit a game-winning, grand slam, record-breaking, out of the ballpark, walk-off homerun!" This prayer reminds us that though I won't be with her in person, I will be with her in spirit. (Becky loves when I pray this way for her. In fact, she has grown to expect it!)

Sample Prayer: "Dear Lord. Thank you for my partner. I pray that you will help him/her with _____. He/she needs your special help and we ask you to do something very specific to meet this need. Thank you. Amen."

THINGS TO BE AWARE OF REGARDING THE *DAILY 5 A'S*:

If your job requires business travel, you can always leave each other voice messages with your part of the *Daily 5 A's*. When at home, choose a mutually agreed upon time of day to do your *Daily 5 A's*. Weekday schedules are often different than weekends. For some, it is best to do them at night, just before getting ready for bed; others prefer morning. When you are dating, it may be a different time than when you get married. Be careful to keep the *Daily 5 A's* to under five minutes or you'll be tempted to avoid them, claiming they take too long. If you want to do an extended *Daily 5 A's*, (for more than five minutes,) only do so by mutual agreement. For example, Becky and I walk three times a week. Most often, on our walk we will go through our *Daily 5 A's* in ten or fifteen minutes, but only by mutual agreement. On the days we don't walk, we usually complete our *Daily 5 A's* in three or four minutes. Our goal, either way, is to remain consistent and daily with them.

Example of the Daily 5 A's:

Mike: Could we do our *Daily 5 A's* now?

Kristin: Sure. How about I start today? I would like to affirm you in how nice you look in your new shirt today. I like it. (*Affirmation*)

Mike: Thank you. Thank you very much. I would like to affirm you for yesterday when I told you that my brother and friends might be getting together to watch the playoffs and I asked you if you are O.K. with me going, you said that you were. I really appreciate that. (*Affirmation*)

Kristin: Here is a kiss and a hug. (*Affection*)

Mike:	Thank you, and here is my kiss and hug back. (*Affection*)
Mike:	Is there anything I did today to hurt or frustrate you? (*Apology*)
Kristin:	Actually, yes, I was a little bit frustrated when you said you were going to pick me up at 5 o'clock and you came at 5:30.
Mike:	I am so sorry for frustrating you. Will you please forgive me?"
Kristin:	Yes. Is there any way I irritated, frustrated or hurt you today? (*Apology*)
Mike:	I can't think of anything.
Kristin:	Is there anything I can do for you? (*Ask*)
Mike:	Yes, after class I need to stay and help out with cleanup. Would you be willing to get us lunch?
Kristin:	O.K.
Mike:	Is there anything I can do for you? (*Ask*)
Kristin:	Yes. My tank is empty. Would you mind filling up the car with gas for me?
Mike:	Sure. I will be glad to do that for you.
Kristin:	Is there any *special* way I can pray for you today? (*Amen*)
Mike:	Sure. If you could just keep praying for my test and everything else that is going on at work; it is busy. Pray for a peace and rest and removal of any anxiety, so I can get things done.
Kristin:	Dear Lord, please help Mike to do well on his test and bring him a peace. Help him not be anxious, but experience your presence. Amen.
Mike:	How I can pray for you? (*Amen*)
Kristin:	Please pray that I get the energy I need to prepare for the party tomorrow night.
Mike:	Dear Father, please help Kristin have energy; fill her with strength so she is able to accomplish all she needs to do for the party tomorrow evening. Bless her with your presence. Amen.

Kiss!! (It's nice to end with more affection, just for fun.)

Questions couples ask about the Daily 5 A's:

Q: Does it matter in what order you do the *Daily 5 A's*?

A: No, we prefer that couples begin with either *Affection* or *Affirmation* as these are light-hearted and easy, but we encourage you to experiment with an order that best fits your relationship and schedule.

Q: Do you pray immediately after you share your prayer requests?

A: Yes, we usually ask for prayer and then our partner prays for it, rather than waiting for both to share their requests before praying.

Q: Do you always have to share a hurt or frustration or give an apology?

A: No, often, only one or neither of us has something to share in the third *Daily A*. In fact, it almost feels like an affirmation when we hear each other say, "I can't think of anything."

Q: What do you do when you feel the need to justify yourself or to convince the other person that you feel sorry, or you need longer to discuss?

A: It is difficult to not try to justify yourself. That happens most often when your partner feels there is a reason why the incident happened and he or she wants to talk about it. We suggest that you stick with the formula and say, "I am sorry that I hurt you. Can we talk about this after we get finished with the *Daily 5 A's*?" Remember, the point of the apology is to validate that you are sorry that you hurt the other person, not prove that you were right or wrong. This exercise is to convey that they feel hurt by something you did and you are genuinely sorry for hurting them. Justification is more for ourselves than the other person; we don't want to feel falsely accused. But once you understand that the *Daily 5 A's* are not about accusation nor justification, but about becoming ministers to each other—comforting, accepting, forgiving, and encouraging each other—you will get better at them.

Q: When is the best time of day to share the *Daily 5 A's*?

A: Whenever it works out best for each couple. Some people do them in the morning; many do them after dinner, and still others prefer the very end of the day.

Q: How important is to keep the *Daily 5 A's* within the three-to-five minute time frame?

A: It is very important so you don't turn a fun, daily exercise into a conflict-resolving experience that ends up taking an hour or more. Our goal is that the *Daily 5 A's* become a tradition or habit for couples—a quick way to connect with each other on an intimate level. If you use the *Daily 5 A's* for more than its purpose (to bring up a recurring issue, request help on a long-term project, or turn it into a prayer meeting,) one of you will begin to avoid them. As mentioned previously, you can either (1) mutually agree on an extended time to do your *Daily 5 A's*, or (2) agree to discuss those things that require significant attention at a later time.

 Couple Assignment

Commit to sharing the Daily 5 A's *with your partner every day for the next week. At the end of the week, discuss the observations, feelings, and experiences you had while sharing the* Daily 5 A's. *Did you find them mechanical, difficult, enjoyable, awkward, and/or helpful?*

 Individual Reflection

Have you reluctantly or willingly participated in sharing the Daily 5 A's *with your partner this past week? Explain. Have you found it difficult to initiate the* Daily 5 A's? *If so, why? Which of the* Daily 5 A's *did you enjoy the most and why?*

1. David Olsen, et al., The Couple Checkup, (Nashville, TN: Thomas Nelson, 2008) 23.

2. John Gottman, Why Marriages Succeed or Fail, (New York, New York: Fireside, 1994) 57.

3. Gottman 57.

4. Willard Harley, Love Busters, (Grand Rapids, MI: Revell, 2002) 21.

 **2**

finances and budgets

It's very common for seriously dating or engaged couples to have different approaches to spending and saving money. While growing up and as single adults each person forms specific saving and spending habits. Therefore, once a couple begins to discuss marriage, it is very important for them to talk about how they will merge and manage their finances.

The planning of the wedding will often reveal how differently partners think about money. For example, it is likely that the woman will focus on the intricate details of the ceremony and reception, including how little or much her dress will cost, the type of flowers they can afford and how much they can spend on the cake. The man might be thinking about the overall cost of the wedding and honeymoon and the impact it will have on their savings.

Finances are a significant aspect of every marriage relationship therefore, this chapter is designed to get you talking about such complex issues as:

- debt (current and future)
- savings accounts (current, future, merging, etc.)
- the use and number of credit cards
- charitable giving (current and projected commitments)
- retirement and savings plans (current and future)
- large purchases
- vacations (honeymoon, family reunions, upcoming weddings, etc.)

A BIBLICAL PERSPECTIVE OF FINANCES AND BUDGET

One of the best perspectives you can have regarding money is to understand that everything you have has been given to you by God. He entrusts you with money and asks you to be good managers of His resources. A biblical perspective of money keeps you from holding on too tight or fearing that you won't have enough.

Not only do I encourage couples to pray about any decisions that involve money, I also want you to ask God to assist you in creating a budget that reflects your values. A budget will help you achieve your goals. It will reflect your priorities and passions, and manage your cash flow. It should include current and future expenditures such as purchasing a home, saving for children, vacation funds and the purchase of life insurance. If you are currently in debt, your budget should reflect your plan for becoming debt-free.

Proverbs 3:9-10 *"Honor the Lord with your wealth, with the first fruits of all your crops; then your barns will be filled to overflowing, and your vats will brim over with new wine."*

Proverbs 13:11 *"Dishonest money dwindles away, but he who gathers money little by little makes it grow."*

Ecclesiastes 5:10 *"Whoever loves money never has money enough; whoever loves wealth is never satisfied with his income. This too is meaningless."*

RESPONSIBILITY FOR FINANCES

Before you get married, an important decision you will need to make is who is going to pay the bills and manage your joint finances. After you get married, we recommend that the more detailed person manage the bills. For at least six months we strongly suggest that both partners review the bills *together every month*, as well as review your budget and compare your goals with your current and/or projected income. This "check-up" keeps both partners aware of your current financial situation and allows you to make any necessary or urgent revisions to your budget.

Areas of Financial Temptation:

ATM and Credit Card Use
It is very easy to insert a debit card into an ATM machine to get quick cash. We've all been tempted by the illusion that we're not withdrawing "that much" money. But if you repeatedly withdraw twenty-dollar bills—that are not in your budget—it will add up very quickly to perhaps an unexpected $200 shortfall at the end of the month. If you use the ATM, make sure you keep track of the receipts and withdraw only agreed-upon funds.

Credit card misuse has an even greater penalty—both because they are tempting to use for impulsive expenditures and they can require high-interest rates. Especially early in your relationship, I suggest that credit cards be used only for travel, emergencies and for agreed-upon purchases.

Comparison with Others
It is easy to want what others have, but jealousy can quickly turn into greed, impulsive spending and debt. Ultimately, it can ruin your budget and your good credit. The temptation to envy is so strong that God made a commandment to help protect us from the damage it can do. Exodus 20:17 says, "You shall not covet your neighbor's house..."[4] We encourage couples to guard their hearts and minds, even with their wedding planning. For example, attending other weddings may tempt you to desire what you can't afford. But if you stay responsible within your budget from the very beginning of your relationship, you have a greater chance of maintaining similar spending and saving behavior throughout your married life.

Wanting Some Degree of Independence
While I recommend that couples combine their incomes after they marry, I also suggest that each partner has a personal allowance. Because you are coming from complete independence to mutual

dependence, some level of personal spending money is healthy. For example, perhaps one of you is a *saver* and the other is a *spender*. Personal spending money allows for your differences and enables you freedom to buy yourself or your partner something without having to account for it. Allowance money is yours to do with whatever you want without the accountability of your partner.

Disclosure about Finances:

No matter how uncomfortable you feel, it is necessary to disclose any and all debt to your partner. As a counselor, I have seen partners conceal debt from each other, only later to have it create major trust issues between them. You cannot be afraid to ask the difficult questions of each other such as, "Have you paid all of your taxes?" or "Do you owe anyone money—parents, friends, colleagues, banks, credit unions, or credit cards?" and "How many credit cards do you have?"

Admittedly, financial differences often result in significant disagreements. Therefore, I recommend that if you experience escalated emotions while moving through this chapter, simply proceed through this chapter's assignments by using the *8 Steps to Conflict Resolution* (Chapter Four), which allows you to empathize with each other as well as brainstorm "win-win" solutions.

Additionally, I recommend that you spend extra time on this subject by reviewing the suggested financial resources listed in this chapter and in the Bibliography.

 Couple Assignment

Using the sample budget worksheet, fill in the spaces for each category based on your projected joint income and expenses after marriage. (In some areas you will have to estimate based on the market values of rentals, utilities, or employment, but do not let the estimates hinder you from completing this assignment. Ask your married friends about current costs or search online for comparable expenditures so that you have a fairly accurate assessment of your future budget.)

Then discuss the following questions:

1. How did your parents manage money?

2. Do you tend to be more of a *saver* or a *spender*?

3. What percentage of your income would you like to invest for retirement?

4. What percentage of your income would you like to deposit in short-term savings?

5. What percentage of your income do you plan on giving to charity? Which ones? How often and how much will you give to your church, non-profit organizations, etc.?

6. Do you plan on having a joint checking account or individual accounts?

7. Will you combine your incomes into one savings account?

8. Have you disclosed all of your assets and liabilities with your partner? (Ex: credit cards, personal loans, bank loans, automobile loans, etc.)

9. If you have differences regarding finances, how do you plan to resolve them?

Monthly Budget Worksheet

Income After Taxes:

His	$_____	"His" Other	$_____
Hers	$_____	"Hers" Other	$_____

Total Income: $

Expenses:

Food		**Gifts**	
Groceries	$_____	Birthdays	$_____
Restaurants	$_____	Anniversary	$_____
Delivery	$_____	Christmas	$_____
Housing Expenses		Misc.	$_____
Mortgage/Rent	$_____	**Insurance**	
Taxes	$_____	Homeowners	$_____
Electric	$_____	or Renters	$_____
Water	$_____	Medical/Dent.	$_____
Gas	$_____	Life	$_____
Phone	$_____	**Personal**	
Cell Phone	$_____	Haircuts	$_____
Cable	$_____	Manicure	$_____
Assoc. Fee	$_____	Counseling	$_____
Repairs	$_____	Savings	$_____
Appliances	$_____	Other	$_____
Misc.	$_____	**Allowances**	
Automobile		Hers	$_____
Car 1 Pymt	$_____	His	$_____
Car 2 Pymt	$_____	Kids	$_____
Tolls	$_____	**Entertainment**	
Gas	$_____	Shows	$_____
Repairs	$_____	Vacations	$_____
Lic./Regis.	$_____	Health Club	$_____
Insurance	$_____	Pets	$_____
Clothing		Other	$_____
New – His	$_____	**Debt**	
New – Hers	$_____	Loans	$_____
New – Kids	$_____	Loans	$_____
Dry Cleaning	$_____	Other	$_____
Education	$_____	Tithing	$_____

Total Expenses $

Total Income	($_____) minus
Total Expenses	($_____) =
	$_____

24   Seriously Dating or Engaged

Individual Reflection

In the process of doing the Budget Worksheet with your partner, how did you feel? How similar or different are you from your partner's financial attitudes and practices? As you prepare for marriage, what changes do you have to make regarding finances? Do you or your partner need further counsel in this area? If so, consider seeking out local counsel and review the listed resources.

Common Questions couples ask regarding finances:

Q: How do you create a budget when you have a variable income or work on commission?

A: Assuming that you have some kind of a track record, review what you earned the last few years and use this as your guide. I recommend that you base your budget using conservative estimates.

Q: We are considering buying a car and possibly a home *before we marry.* We are wondering if there is a problem we can't foresee?

A: I do not recommend that you make large purchases or even merge accounts before you marry. I know couples who had purchased cars and homes and called off their engagement before the wedding.

Q: How much savings do we need to have before we get married?

A: Financial experts suggest that couples have enough money saved to get them through four to six months in case of loss of job or another unexpected circumstance.

Q: Do we save first if we have credit card debt or do we try to get rid of the debt first?

A: It depends on the interest you are paying on the debt. I recommend that you save some amount money each month, while being as aggressive as possible to pay off your debt.

Q: Is having a high level of credit card debt a red flag for not getting married?

A: It can be. It can indicate a weakness such as an uncontrolled habit or an addiction. Spending can be addictive. If your partner can't explain the details of the debt, it might be a red flag. You must disclose everything and together make an assessment. I strongly encourage couples in these situations to meet with a financial advisor or a counselor.

Recommended Financial Resources (see details in Bibliography):

Crown Ministries (www.crown.org)

Debt Free Living by Larry Burkett (www.cfcministry.org)

The Treasure Principle by Randy Alcorn

The Complete Financial Guide for Young Couples by Larry Burkett

NOTES..

 **3**

knowing each other

Seriously dating and engaged couples often assume they know *"all there is to know"* about each other. Yet after diligently working through the material in this chapter, they're very surprised at how much *more* there is to discover about each other.

This chapter is designed to help you better understand your own and your partner's *Personality Types, Love Languages, Similarities and Differences* and *Family of Origin.*

PERSONALITY TYPES

After three decades of working with seriously dating, engaged, and married couples (and over thirty-one years of marriage to Becky,) I'm convinced that understanding each other's personality type is one the most important factors in maintaining a successful, lifelong relationship. In fact, current research suggests it may be the most significant factor in marital happiness.[1]

I've even found that specific problems such as poor communication, financial disagreements, and lack of sexual intimacy—issues that normally cause conflict between couples—can pale in comparison to the problems that personality differences can cause. In fact, many conflicts arise simply because couples don't understand their partner's personality type. In the beginning of most relationships, partners appreciate each other's strengths. But later, usually right after the honeymoon, couples tend to focus on his or her partner's weaknesses.

- *Before* the marriage she says: "He's a man of few words, but he's a great listener. I love to talk so it works out great."

  After the marriage she says: "He doesn't have much to say and I end up having to carry the entire conversation."

- *Before* the marriage he says, "She is such a great conversationalist."

  After the marriage he says, "She needs to talk about everything. In fact, she goes on and on and on. It drives me crazy."

If you don't understand each other's personality type, it can hinder your love life for years! I recently counseled a couple that had been married for 25 years, but never fully understood each other's personality strengths and weaknesses. After helping them understand each other's personality types, they reported an immediate increase in intimacy and a much deeper satisfaction in their relationship. They truly wished they had been aware of this information when they first got married, realizing how it could have made their lives together much easier and more fun.

Becky and I encourage you to gain as much knowledge as you can about your partner's personality at the beginning stages of your relationship, as well as develop a plan to deal with your strengths, weaknesses, and differences.

Understanding CORE Personality Types

In this section, you will be asked to work through the following personality concepts:

1. Identify your partner's primary personality types.

2. Become familiar with the strengths and weaknesses of each personality type.

3. Predict specific personality behaviors for you and your partner.

4. Focus on your own, as well as your partner's strengths.

5. Establish a plan to deal with your own, as well as your partner's weaknesses.

Taking a CORE Personality Inventory

There are a variety of personality inventories including the Myers Briggs Personality Test, DISC, or *Personality Plus Profile* by Florence and Marita Littauer. Each of these inventories categorizes personality behaviors into various types. The Myers Briggs Test uses sixteen types. Other inventories use four or five factors. Becky and I have designed the *CORE Personality Inventory* that incorporates four primary personality types:

1. **Charger**
2. **Outgoing**
3. **Responsible**
4. **Easy-going**

Take and score the following CORE Personality Inventory. After taking the inventory, finish reading the information in this chapter and then discuss the assignment that follows.

CORE PERSONALITY INVENTORY

Instructions:

1. Please complete the personality inventory below and score accordingly. They will each have their own book.

2. Working across the rows from left to right, rate the words according to which characteristic best describes you. Put a **3** by the word that **best describes you**, a **2** by the word that is your second choice, a **1** by the word that minimally describes you and a **0** by the word that least describes you. Put a **circle** around the word that most characterizes your partner.

     EXAMPLE: _3_ risk taker   _0_ precise   _2_ talkative   (_1_ calm)

3. **Circle** the one trait on each line that you feel is *closest to the personality trait of your* ***partner***.

Strengths: *(remember go from left to right.)*

1. __ calm	__ precise	__ talkative	__ risk taker
2. __ sensitive	__ leader	__ safe	__ fast
3. __ popular	__ accurate	__ confident	__ tolerant
4. __ nice	__ optimistic	__ assertive	__ orderly
5. __ self-assured	__ entertaining	__ patient	__ serious
6. __ humble	__ gentle	__ convincing	__ driven
7. __ decisive	__ playful	__ loyal	__ helpful
8. __ adventurous	__ devoted	__ enthusiastic	__ obliging
9. __ persistent	__ disciplined	__ motivator	__ satisfied
10. __ deep	__ pleasant	__ productive	__ sociable
11. __ fun	__ efficient	__ peaceful	__ achiever

Weaknesses:

12. __ bossy	__ poor listener	__ bashful	__ disconnected
13. __ hard to please	__ can't relax	__ indecisive	__ impatient
14. __ domineering	__ fearful	__ skeptical	__ poor follow-up
15. __ distracted	__ slow	__ demanding	__ introvert
16. __ lazy	__ need to win	__ too sensitive	__ undisciplined
17. __ stubborn	__ forgetful	__ depressed	__ timid
18. __ critical	__ show off	__ unenthusiastic	__ argumentative
19. __ moody	__ impulsive	__ insensitive	__ reluctant
20. __ disorganized	__ detached	__ harsh	__ revengeful
21. __ proud	__ perfectionist	__ unreliable	__ doubtful
22. __ often late	__ too competitive	__ inflexible	__ indifferent

CORE Personality Inventory: Scoring Sheet

Look for the word on the previous page and put the number in the blank that is next to the same word below. <u>NOTE</u>: *The words will be in the same row, but in different order. Circle the word you chose for your partner's number one personality trait.*

Strengths:

1. __ risk taker	__ talkative	__ precise	__ calm
2. __ leader	__ fast	__ sensitive	__ safe
3. __ confident	__ popular	__ accurate	__ tolerant
4. __ assertive	__ optimistic	__ orderly	__ nice
5. __ self-assured	__ entertaining	__ serious	__ patient
6. __ driven	__ convincing	__ humble	__ gentle
7. __ decisive	__ playful	__ loyal	__ helpful
8. __ adventurous	__ enthusiastic	__ devoted	__ obliging
9. __ persistent	__ motivates	__ disciplined	__ satisfied
10. __ productive	__ sociable	__ deep	__ pleasant
11. __ achiever	__ fun	__ efficient	__ peaceful
TOTAL	TOTAL	TOTAL	TOTAL
____ STRENGTHS	____STRENGTHS	____STRENGTHS	____STRENGTHS

Weaknesses:

12. __ bossy	__ poor listener	__ bashful	__ disconnected
13. __ can't relax	__ impatient	__ hard to please	__ indecisive
14. __ domineering	__ poor follow-up	__ skeptical	__ fearful
15. __ demanding	__ distracted	__ introvert	__ slow
16. __ need to win	__ undisciplined	__ too sensitive	__ lazy
17. __ stubborn	__ forgetful	__ depressed	__ timid
18. __ argumentative	__ show off	__ critical	__ unenthusiastic
19. __ insensitive	__ impulsive	__ moody	__ reluctant
20. __ harsh	__ disorganized	__ revengeful	__ detached
21. __ proud	__ unreliable	__ perfectionist	__ doubtful
22. __ too competitive	__ often late	__ inflexible	__ indifferent
TOTAL	TOTAL	TOTAL	TOTAL
____ WEAKNESS	____WEAKNESS	____WEAKNESS	____WEAKNESS
+	+	+	+
____ STRENGTHS	____ STRENGTHS	____ STRENGTHS	____ STRENGTHS
=	=	=	=
____C	____O	____R	____E
CHARGER	OUTGOING	RESPONSIBLE	EASY-GOING

Characteristics of each personality type:

The Charger:

A Charger personality has exceptional vision and the energy to achieve, produce, and to forge ahead in the face of barriers. The Charger is a "mover and a shaker." He or she is often the chairman of the Board or the CEO of a corporation. They are self-starters, risk takers and problem solvers. Chargers can be bossy, domineering and overly competitive. They also have a difficult time relaxing.

The Outgoing:

The Outgoing personality is characterized as the "fun" one. They are the life of the party. Enthusiastic and sociable, they have a lot of energy and excitement and bring joy to everyone. They struggle with being on-time, staying focused, listening attentively and they often lose their possessions. They are very conversational, but prone to interrupting others. Though they are flexible, their flexibility can turn almost anything into chaos.

Responsible:

The Responsible personality diligently takes care of details. They are usually on-time, always have a balanced checkbook, complete their homework on time (or even early), and are very caring and sensitive. They tend to be more bashful. Known as perfectionists, they are often difficult to please; but admittedly are the hardest on themselves. The Responsible personality type wants to have or get it right. Of all the personality types, they can be the most skeptical. They tend to be sensitive, analytical people with a propensity toward music and the arts. They are susceptible to depressive thoughts or feelings, usually because things are not the way they "should" be. Fairness is very important to them. They often have to work on being more gracious and flexible, and even small changes can create anxiety for the Responsible type.

Easy-going:

The Easy-going personality types are the peacemakers or the peacekeepers in the world. They are kickback people who exist to help and support others. They are congenial, gentle, patient and kind. They are often falsely accused of being lazy, but often need prodding to get things done. Though willing to help others with almost anything, they will need a nap afterward.

An Example of the Personality Types working together:

If you asked a room full of people to help you, the *Easy-going* and the *Responsible* personalities will immediately offer their services. While the *Easy-going* personality will collect papers or carry chairs to the back of the room, the *Responsible* personality will make sure that the chairs are in a straight line or a neat stack. But the *Charger* will most likely be headed off to another scheduled appointment and the *Outgoing* personality will be unaware of the work being done, immersed in a conversation with one or more acquaintances or even strangers.

The following chart will help you see the common tendencies of each of the personality type.

	STRENGTHS	WEAKNESSES
CHARGER		
Wants Responsibility Wants Affirmation Wants to Achieve	Decisive Independent Leader Practical Determined Risk Taker	Confident Dominating Stubborn Tough Impatient Harsh
OUTGOING		
Wants Approval Wants Social Time Wants to have Fun	Stimulating Enthusiastic Fun Outgoing Personable Communicators	Show off Egotistical Irresponsible Poor listener Forgetful Unrealistic
RESPONSIBLE		
Wants quiet / alone time Wants admiration Wants efficiency	Thorough Persistent Orderly Serious Industrious Accurate	Perfectionist Inflexible Introvert Moralistic Critical Too Sensitive
EASY-GOING		
Wants Appreciation Wants to take a nap Wants Peace	Supportive Quiet Dependable Reliable Agreeable Patient	Lacks assertiveness Fearful Dependent Timid Retiring Lazy

How each personality type gets rejuvenated or recharged:

Charger - Recharged by Personal Time
Outgoing - Recharged by Social Time
Responsible - Recharged by Physical Activity
Easy-going - Recharged by Relaxation

How each personality type reacts to stress:

	INITIAL REACTION	IF PROBLEM PERSISTS
Charger	Demand	Withdraw
Outgoing	Attack	Comply
Responsible	Withdraw	Demand
Easy-going	Comply	Attack

How to understand each personality types strengths and weaknesses:

1. View each other in terms of their strengths, not weaknesses.

2. When you experience your partner's weaknesses, identify the corresponding strength. (For example, if a person's weakness is inflexibility, concentrate more on their ability to stay focused on a task. When you remind yourself of your partner's strength, you'll understand them better and be less tempted to judge them.)

3. Be available to complement your partner's weaknesses with your strengths. (Example: If your partner is a better organizer, allow them to help you get organized.)

4. A personality strength pushed to the extreme can become a weakness.

5. All personality types have the same amount of strengths and weaknesses. One personality type is not better than another personality type; they are just different from each other.

6. It is important to be aware of your secondary personality type and discuss it with your partner because it also involves a specific range of strengths and weaknesses.

Example of how a couple can accept each other's weaknesses:

Amy is split equally between *Outgoing* and *Charger*. She can be very intense at times. Brian is an *Easy-going/Outgoing*, stronger in the *Easy-going* area. Amy loves that Brian is very calm and able to reel her back in when she feels like the world is ending. He also lovingly picks up the pieces behind her when she is steamrolling and charging toward the goals she has set to accomplish. She, however, can get irritated when Brian wants to take a nap. As a result of understanding their personality types, Amy has agreed to leave more "margin" in her schedule and even read a good book while Brian naps. In this way, they have learned to complement each other's personalities. Understanding their personality types has helped them accept one another and by working through a plan to minimize their personality weaknesses, they experience a much more enjoyable marriage relationship.

Couple Assignment

1. Take and score the following CORE Personality Inventory. *Then sit together with the forms in front of you and share your results. Compare each other's scores, determining how you are similar or dissimilar in each of the four areas.*

2. *Looking at what your partner chose as his or her strengths, share three specific traits that most attract you to him or her and describe how they make you feel when you experience them.*

3. *Next, choose three personality weaknesses (traits) from each of your sheets that you feel might cause a conflict in your relationship.*

4. *Discuss a plan that you both feel would minimize the effect of each of the weaknesses. For example, my Outgoing personality has the weakness of being late. The plan Becky and I developed has several aspects to it. When I realize that am running behind, it's important that I call her and let her know what is happening and what time she can expect me. She also helps me by calling me about a half an hour before she expects me, to alert me of the time. Additionally, I have set my watch 5 minutes ahead to assist me in being more punctual. Finally, when I am late, I apologize quickly and try not to defend myself. When I am late, however, it is her responsibility to not to get irritated but to remind herself that (1) I am an Outgoing and not purposely being tardy, and (2) she loves my flexible and fun nature.*

Individual Reflection

What are the predictable positive and negative personality traits of my partner? What am I learning about myself and my partner's personality that is helping me be more accepting and understanding of our weaknesses and strengths? What one personality trait/behavior am I going to struggle with the most?

Q&A

Q: Is there a combination of personality types that can't work well together or resolve their differences?

A: It is not so much the combination of personality types that is important, but the way in which a couple deals with their weaknesses. Of course, if you have extremely high scores in opposite personality types, this will signal that you'll need to make many more relationship adjustments. (A *Charger* is the opposite of an *Easy-going*; a *Responsible* is the opposite of an *Outgoing*.) It's extremely important to be committed to using good communication skills along with the use of the *8 Steps of Conflict Resolution* and understanding each other's personality weaknesses.

Q: What if your partner has alike scores on all four personality types?

A: Having similar scores isn't abnormal. Many people have scores that are evenly distributed. These individuals tend to be more evenly balanced. To better predict his or her behavior, determine the specific traits in each of the four categories that make him or her unique.

LOVE LANGUAGES

For 20 years I bought my mom flowers for her birthday. She was always very kind and thanked me. After her 60th birthday she told me, "I really don't like flowers." Since I had been buying them for her for all those years, I asked her why she didn't like flowers and she said, "Because when the flowers die, I feel sad." I asked her what I could buy her to show her how much I loved her. She said, "I just like it when you send me a card and you write something special on it or just call me." My mother's love language is *Words of Affirmation*. Too bad I didn't know her love language twenty years earlier!

Psychologist Gary Chapman, author of **The Five Love Languages,** helped thousands of couples develop better relationships by revealing that everyone expresses and receives love in different ways. More importantly, he narrowed down each person's primary love language—or the way he or she feels loved—into five categories:

1. Words of Affirmation: Compliments, in either written or verbal form, show appreciation and encouragement to this person who prefers this love language. Notes, letters, and text messages are simple ways to meet their need for love. Affirmations such as "You look so beautiful (or handsome)," or "thank you so much for helping with the dishes," or "that meal was the best," or "you are an awesome cook" also express love to this person. It should be no surprise that criticism is particularly hurtful to this person (and an irritation to just about everyone.)

2. Quality Time: Undivided attention is most important to the person with this primary love language. It is not the quantity of time, but quality of time that matters to them. Date nights, mini-vacations, walks, talk-time and shared activities fill their "love account." In fact, they don't want to just go to dinner, they want you to establish good eye contact, become an intentional listener and ask for details. Long periods of time away from each other or excessive time spent with others, rather than together, can be very difficult for the person with this love language. Because quality time can look very different for people, it is better to define what it means to you. For one couple, quality time might be as simple as coming home after work, watching TV together and cuddling on the couch. Another couple may prefer to turn off the TV and have an intimate conversation together.

3. Physical Touch: People with this love language need more physical affection than others. They require physical closeness to feel loved. They might experience this through physical touch (including non-sexual gestures) such as holding hands, shoulder-rubbing, kissing often, hugging and cuddling. Before you marry, if/as you limit your expressions of physical touch, talk about this need in detail. You may want to read the chapter on Sexual Intimacy before proceeding. It is important not to make your partner feel uncomfortable by demanding physical touch.

4. Acts of Service: Tasks, to-dos, helping your extended families, washing the cars, and doing the laundry are ways the person with this love language gets "filled-up." When your partner's love language is Acts of Service, it is important to find out specifically what they would like you to do for them.

Acts of Service include:

• *Fill up the gas tank*	• *Help with a project*	• *Cook for them*
• *Do the dishes*	• *Wash the car*	• *Tidy up a workspace*
• *Open doors for them*	• *Go grocery shopping*	
• *Pull out a chair for them to be seated*	• *Help the other person get organized (if they would like this)*	

5. Receiving Gifts: Throughout the world, gift-giving is a means to communicate love. A gift can say "You are important to me," "I care for you," or "I am thinking about you." Gifts don't necessarily have to be expensive —flowers, a rose, a favorite magazine, a book, favorite candy bar or even something homemade can say "I love you" to the person who speaks this kind of love language.

Discovering your partner's love language is the secret to a meaningful relationship. Though I've listed and described Chapman's five love languages for you to identify the way you feel loved, I suggest that you take the *Love Language Test* at http://www.afo.net/hftw-lovetest.asp. Share it with your partner.

Couple Assignment

Rank the love languages in the order of you and your partner's importance.

His	Her
1.	1.
2.	2.
3.	3.
4.	4.
5.	5.

What are three specific behaviors your partner would like you to do for them based on his or her top two love languages?

Primary Language: _____
1._____
_____
2._____
_____
3._____
_____

Secondary Language: _____
1._____
_____
2._____
_____
3._____
_____

Primary Language: _____
1._____
_____
2._____
_____
3._____
_____

Secondary Language: _____
1._____
_____
2._____
_____
3._____
_____

Individual Reflection

Based on your primary and secondary love languages, reflect on those times when you felt especially loved by your partner. What made you feel this way? Set aside time to share two of those experiences with your partner.

SIMILARITIES AND DIFFERENCES

By now, you might be thinking you've discovered everything there is to know about each other, but depending upon how long you've been dating or engaged, there is still much more to learn! Though talking about your similarities and differences can actually be a fun exercise, more importantly, it is another great opportunity to understand each other better.

 Couple Assignment

*I recommend that you go through each item on the Similarities and Differences Worksheet in detail. Don't try to do this exercise in one or even two sittings. Take a month or more to process them. As you discuss each item decide whether you are **very similar VS**, **similar S**, **different D** or **extremely different ED** on each item. Talk about how you might have a conflict with certain areas of difference. Take notes as you talk about these together and if you have a mentor couple, a counselor or pastor working through this material with you, also share your insights with them. Ask them if they have any experiences that might be of help to you.*

*Discuss the following list of topics and issues in detail. Next to each item mark whether you think you are **Very Similar VS**, **Similar S**, **Different D** or **Extremely Different ED**.*

Similarities and Differences Worksheet

____Family traditions	____Holidays celebrated
____How and where holidays are celebrated	____Hobbies
____Sports Involvement	____Recreation
____Television (types of shows and amount of time spent viewing)	____Eating out
____Types of food	____Movies
____Time spent at work	____Time spent at home
____Travel	____Budgeting
____Spending	____Saving
____Type of automobiles	____Reading
____Past Education	____Education for our children
____Children's education, private or public	____Our intelligence
____Socio-economic background	____Politics
____Alcohol consumption	____Attitude about alcohol
____Cleanliness	____Orderliness

____Importance of physical fitness   ____Health attitudes

____Personalities   ____Church attendance

____Church involvement   ____Spirituality

____Involvement with family members   ____Involvement with parents

____Involvement with friends   ____Number of friends

____Time spent with friends   ____Opposite sex friendship

____Number of children desired and when   ____Consideration of adoption

____Geographic area in which to live   ____Disciplining of children

____Purchase home verse renting home   ____Adventure

____Risk taking   ____Communication

____Communication online   ____Facebook and Twitter

____Number of sleeping hours required   ____Sleep patterns

____Naps   ____Temperature of room during day

____Temperature of room for sleeping   ____Attitude and involvement with drugs

____Attitude and involvement with smoking

Individual Reflection

How do you feel about the similarities and differences you discussed? Do you have more similarities than differences? If you have more differences, what do you feel your next steps might be to accept and adjust to each other?

FAMILY OF ORIGIN

Your family of origin is key in understanding why you do many of the things you do. Asking questions of your partner and probing for a deeper understanding and knowledge of your partner's background is essential to knowing each other. For example, the way you act or react can often result from a childhood pattern or a "childlike" way of thinking. How you coped with your family of origin as a child can also easily create problems in our current relationships, especially in your most intimate ones.

Present-day hurts within marriage are often brought about by old wounds. These negative past experiences or learned behaviors can fuel our current feelings causing overreactions. Often we aren't aware of the connection of a current reaction to a past painful event or situation. The following is a list of some of the most difficult scenarios:

Substance Abuse	Alcoholism	Racism
Pride	Physical Abuse	Sexual Abuse
Emotional Abuse	Verbal Abuse	Rebellion
Gambling	Procrastination	Excessive spending
Workaholics	Excessive talking	Critically spirited
Angry outbursts	Avoidance	Television or computer addict
Sexual addictions	Unfaithfulness	

What was passed down to us not only affects us, but our children, our grandchildren and great-grandchildren. With God's help, we have the power to break these generational cycles of sin. Here are five steps you can take:

1. Recognize the tendency in your own life.

2. Take responsibility and admit it.

3. Forgive your parents for their iniquity (it was probably passed down to them by their parents or grandparents).

4. Ask God to help you change.

5. Find someone who will keep you accountable.

Perhaps you can identify with Jen's story:

Growing up in Jen's house was like taking a daily walk through a mine field. If her mom's patience began to wear thin, her mom would yell. She'd yell at Jen, her siblings, Jen's dad and even the dog! When Jen got married and she'd become frustrated, her first inclination was to start yelling. One day, in the middle of an angry episode, she realized she was out of control. She stopped and asked her husband, Grant, for forgiveness. As Jen prayed about her weakness and talked with her parents about controlling her anger, they each realized this inclination for uncontrolled anger had been passed down from generation to generation. With that understanding came forgiveness between Jen and her parents and the confidence to seek God's renewal and strength to overcome this sin. Jen began to pray about this issue every day and learned to stop before her anger escalated and say, "In the name of Jesus, I am not going to yell." One of her favorite verses became Exodus 34:6 "… the LORD, the compassionate and gracious God, slow to anger, abounding in love and faithfulness, maintaining love to thousands, and forgiving wickedness, rebellion and sin…" She also reminded herself often of the warning in verse 7, "Yet he does not leave the guilty unpunished; he punishes the children and their children for the sin of the fathers to the third and fourth generation." Understanding the role her parents' past behavior played in her current relationship with her husband has helped Jen heal from those wounds and develop healthy relationship skills.

 Couple Assignment

I suggest praying with each other before you discuss these questions. Ask the Lord to open your heart and mind to the positive traditions and family traits that you wish to continue in your new family and to honestly admit iniquities that you need to break. Remember that the iniquities will probably come up most when you are stressed, frustrated, irritated or angry. It is better to know about them and be proactive than to be blindsided, having to deal with them in the heat of a battle.

These questions are not meant to cover all needed areas of discussion, but they will get you started on the road to discovery.

1. Make a list of the names of your mother and father, their ages and any step-parents, etc.

2. Is there anything special about their relationship? How did you see your parents treat each other? Positive or negative?

3. Regarding your parent's relationship, what would you *like* to see carried forward in your future family?

4. What would you *not like* to see carried forward in your future family?

5. As a child, describe your relationship with your parents. How has it changed? What is it like today? Describe an ideal relationship with your parents.

6. How has your relationship with them affected you? How do you think your relationship with each parent will affect your marriage?

7. Make a list of your sibling's names, ages and how you relate to each of them.

8. Share some of the positive aspects of these sibling relationships that you want to carry forward.

9. What are some things you do not want to carry forward?

10. What are some family traditions or experiences that you would *like* to see carried on in your future family?

11. What are some traditions or experiences that you would *not want* to see carried on in your future family?

12. Were there any abuses in your family? (Drugs, alcohol, sexual, physical, emotional, etc.) What affect do you think they have had on you? (If you are experiencing a negative impact from your past, I encourage you to see a pastor or a Christian counselor.)

13. What roles did your parents assume in your family?

14. What roles did the children play?

15. What roles do you see you and your spouse and children carrying on in the future? Which ones would you not want to carry on?

16. What positive characteristics do you bring from your family of origin?

17. What negative traits do you see yourself bringing to your family in the future? What might you do to help yourself overcome some of these?

18. Do you and your parents, siblings, family members have any unresolved issues at this time? If so, what are they and what might you do to resolve them?

19. What has been the spiritual formation of your family as a child? Do you want to carry that on in your future family? Explain.

20. Are there any family illnesses, tragedies, experiences or histories that your partner should know about?

21. Is there anything else from your family of origin that might affect your future relationship or your future family?

22. Do you desire children of your own? If so, how many and what would be the ideal time and spacing?

23. Did you develop a reaction that is more a "flight-response" or a "fight-response" to family difficulties? Why do you think you developed that response? What do you think you will be able to do to change that response in the future? How could your partner assist you in making that adjustment?

24. Sometimes we develop sensitivities from our past. For example, if our parents were overly controlling we might be very sensitive to feeling controlled by our spouse. Other sensitivities might include the feeling of being mistrusted, feeling left or abandoned, jealousy, feeling left-out or ignored, feeling used, feeling taken advantage or feeling as if others talked down to you. Which of the above might you consider your "Hot Buttons?"

25. Do you think you have developed a "people-pleasing," or "avoidance" or "challenging" response to relationship conflict? What do you think you could do to minimize any of these tendencies? What might your partner do to assist you?

Individual Reflection

Each of us will have a tendency to act either just like our parents or the very opposite, especially during times of stress, frustration and anger. Regardless of what your partner does in the future, refrain from accusing them of being "just like your" mother or father, brother or sister (if this is meant to be a negative comment.) Are you willing to remove this statement from your vocabulary?

What did I learn about myself by going through the Family of Origin questions? What decisions do I need to make as a result of the insights I gained?

---

1 Luo, Shanhong, and Eva Klohnen. "University of Iowa Study." <u>Journal of Personality and Social Psychology</u>, 88 2 (2005): 304.

4

resolving conflicts and managing anger

Learning to manage and resolve conflict is critical to enjoying a loving and successful relationship. So it should be no surprise that poor and ineffective communication, as well as unchecked anger will significantly and negatively impact your relationship. In fact, *Love Busters'* author, psychologist Willard Harley, identifies angry outbursts as one of the most destructive behaviors in marriage.[1]

In an angry state, a physiological process occurs. Your body doesn't know the difference between a relationship struggle and a physical threat. It will react in the same way to either situation. The blood will leave the front portion of your brain and flood to the large muscles. Adrenalin will cause your heartbeat to race and your breathing to increase. Without blood in the front of your brain, your ability to think logically is diminished and you are prone to doing and saying things you'll later regret.

In addition, anger is a secondary emotion. It is a reaction to feeling hurt, irritated, rejected, frustrated, jealous or abandoned. Therefore, in order to control anger, you must identify the feelings that preceded it. Very often, merely asking yourself, "What am I feeling *in addition to* anger?" allows you to recognize the underlying emotions that have caused you to feel angry. Therefore, couples must be proactive in handling their emotions.

In this chapter, we provide you with three proven strategies for managing different levels of anger and conflict. Though the systems might initially feel mechanical, be assured that hundreds of couples have utilized these strategies and reported that they no longer find themselves escalating out-of-control.

Strategy I: Use a Statement to Diffuse Anger
Strategy II: Use a Time-out Process to Manage Anger
Strategy III: Use a Systematic Approach to Resolve Conflict

STRATEGY I: USE A STATEMENT TO DIFFUSE ANGER

Every couple should have a simple and immediate strategy for handling anger.

One of the quickest methods Becky and I have found to help us counteract unexpected surges of anger is to use a memorized "diffusing statement" that warns us not to hurt each other. In advance, we've agreed to use one or two statements that put an immediate pause on any escalating moments, such as:

- "I love you and you love me, and we don't want to hurt each other."
- "I feel like we are under a spiritual attack." (*See the 8 Steps to Conflict Resolution.*)
- "There is no blood in my brain."
- "Can we take a 10-minute time-out?" (*See 3 Step Time-Out Process.*)

Couple Assignment

Take a few minutes to brainstorm one or two diffusing statements that you both agree will effectively keep you from escalating into an argument. Write them below and then put your initials and the date below the statements as a way of showing mutual agreement.

We agree to use the following statement(s) when we begin to escalate:

_____

_____

Initials _____ Date _____

On those occasions when you have diffused an outburst of anger by using an agreed upon statement, but one or both of you still cannot communicate calmly with each other, proceed with the following anger management strategy by taking a short time-out apart from each other.

STRATEGY II: USE A TIME-OUT PROCESS TO MANAGE ANGER

The goal in each of these strategies is not only to help you manage your anger, but to process it. By taking the necessary time to process your anger, you will be less tempted to hurt yourself by suppressing or "stuffing" it. (Suppressing your anger can result in depression, migraine headaches, and other physical and emotional problems.)

Time-outs are designed to do just that—give you time to process your anger. Time-outs are not avoidance tactics. They are not opportunities for going on long runs, talking on the phone with someone else, or watching television. Although these activities might diminish your anger, they are not usually helpful in resolving it.

Therefore, the *Time-out Process* is specifically designed for those situations in which you are still unable to speak to each other in a loving and empathetic manner and more time is needed to process anger. In advance of such moments, choose a designated, safe place to take a time-out and proceed through the following three steps.

Couple Assignment

Where will you each go in moments when you cannot control your emotions? Discuss different scenarios in which you can safely process your anger—while at her place, at his place, in public, in the car, etc.

The 3-Step Time-out Process

1. Calm yourself and get alone.
2. Identify the enemy and your emotions.
3. Speak the truth in love.

Time-out Process Worksheet

Step 1: Calm yourself and get alone.

A. Take a few deep breaths and count to 10 or to 1000. Do whatever it takes to keep from attacking or over-reacting. The goal of this step is to keep from attacking your partner; from judging, criticizing, and allowing destructive anger.

B. Go to a designated place where you can be alone with God and process your anger. The purpose of this step is to get connected with God and get your anger under His control.

C. Pray. Ask God to help you manage your anger by helping you identify the hurt, frustration, or irritation behind it.

> *"God, I ask you to soften my heart and actions. Help me get a handle on my emotions. I*
> *commit to grow in character. Help me to resolve my hurt and anger, not judge nor accuse,*
> *not take revenge or hold on to any bitterness."* (This is a prayer based on Romans 5:1-5.)

Step 2: Identify the enemy and your emotions.

Becky and I not only believe that God loves us and created us, but we also believe that we live a world influenced by evil. In the Gospel of John, Jesus called this evil entity our enemy who comes to steal, kill and destroy us.

As you proceed through the Time-out Process, we will ask you to look at anger from the following biblical perspective: it is your enemy's goal to get couples to attack, over-react and accuse each other. On the contrary, it is God's goal for you to love, support and become your partner's advocate. Once you consider that you have an enemy who wants to destroy your relationship, you'll be much more motivated to become an advocate for your partner, rather than an accuser of him or her.

A. *Consider that you have an evil enemy and it's not your partner!*

Ephesians 6:12 says, "We do not fight against flesh and blood but against principalities and powers."

B. *Ask, "What am I feeling in addition to anger?"*

Are you feeling afraid, threatened, ignored, disappointed, misunderstood, overlooked, pressured, defeated, used, dominated, rejected, hurt, cut-off, cheated, irritated, controlled, jealous, accused or falsely accused?

C. *Ask, "What behaviors am I being tempted to use?"*

Am I tempted to attack, judge, withhold, explode, withdraw, give up, criticize, stuff, tease or be sarcastic?

D. *Ask, "What judgments or accusations am I having toward my partner?*

"They are selfish, lazy…" or, "They are not loving…" or, "They don't care about me…" The natural tendency is to take the role of an accuser. God's desire is for you to become your partner's advocate.

E. *Ask, "How can I stop being an accuser and become an advocate for my partner?"*

What statement am I going to believe to stand against the criticism and judgment? Tell yourself positive statements about your partner, such as, "He/she does love me because …" or "He/she does care, he/she just…"

F. *List any positive evidence or behaviors that your partner exhibits that can counteract the judgments or accusations you're feeling toward them.*

List the ways that your partner cares for you regularly—calling or texting you with encouraging words, preparing a meal for you, making an appointment on your behalf, encouraging you to go to the gym or play golf, or leaving a note for you in your car.

G. *Ask, "When and how have I hurt someone in such a way as to make them feel--angry, emotional, hurt, frustrated--the way I feel right now?"*

This question is designed to elicit an empathetic response and minimize your anger toward your partner.

Step 3: Speak the truth in love.

Remember, the goal of anger management is not merely to control your anger, but to process it so that you can speak with your partner in a loving way. At this juncture, you should be able to return to your partner and communicate in love. Begin by greeting him or her with a hug or a kiss. Then affirm them by sharing one of the positive responses you identified (in **E** or **F** of Step 2) in this *Time-out Process*. After you have affirmed your partner, depending upon the level of hurt or misunderstanding, this disagreement or conflict may be resolved by using the *Intentional-Empathetic Listening Worksheet*. On those occasions, you'll find that forgiveness comes quickly and/or brainstorming win-win solutions comes easily. But, if this is a recurring issue or you are still unable to communicate calmly with your partner, you must move directly to the *8 Steps of Conflict Resolution*.

 Couple Assignment

Talk about how anger was managed in your family of origin. Did you experience avoidance or attacking? As a couple, what barriers do you think you will encounter using this Time-out Process?

The Bible provides powerful relationship advice for couples. In this exercise, the following Proverbs offer insight into anger management and avoidance behavior. Discuss each verse. How might they improve or impact your relationship?

Proverbs 27:5 "Open rebuke is better than hidden love."

Proverbs 20:3 "It is to a man's honor to avoid strife, but every fool is quick to quarrel. "

Galatians 5:22-23 "But the fruit of the spirit is love, joy, peace, patience, kindness, goodness, faithfulness, gentleness and self control."

Proverbs 12:18 "Reckless words pierce like a sword, but the tongue of the wise brings healing."

Proverbs 18:21 "The tongue has the power of life and death, and those who love it will eat its fruit."

Proverbs 17:27 "A man of knowledge uses words with restraint, and a man of understanding is even-tempered."

Proverbs 29:11 "A fool gives full vent to his anger, but a wise man keeps himself under control."

 Individual Reflection

What do you feel (or anticipate feeling) when your partner gets angry with you? What place (or places) did you designate to take your time-out? Go over the Time-out Process, step by step. Do you see or feel any potential barriers to working through this system? If so, consider ways in which you will overcome them.

STRATEGY III: A SYSTEMATIC APPROACH TO CONFLICT RESOLUTION

In the book, *Fighting for Your Marriage*, the authors claim, "It's not how much you love one another, how good your sex life is or what problems you have with money that best predicts the future quality of your marriage... The best predictor of marital success is the way you handle conflicts and disagreements."[1]

Conflict is one of the most important predictors of the quality and future of a couple's relationship. The question is not *if* you will experience conflict, but how you will handle it.

The *8 Steps for Conflict Resolution* are specifically designed to protect a couple's intimacy by providing steps for safe communication that control anger and minimize interruption or defensiveness. Additionally, the *8 Steps to Conflict Resolution Worksheet* will help you master the process of resolving conflict, but only if you completely follow each step in order. Avoid taking any short cuts.

 ## The 8 Steps to Conflict Resolution

STEP 1: Check your anger.

STEP 2: Check the time.

STEP 3: Call on God immediately.

STEP 4: Proceed with the *Intentional-Empathetic Listening Worksheet*.

STEP 5: Formulate a statement that clearly identifies the conflict for both partners.

STEP 6: Brainstorm possible solutions.

STEP 7: Agree upon a solution.

STEP 8: Try your solution and evaluate its effectiveness.

Detailed Explanation of the 8 Steps to Conflict Resolution

STEP 1: Check your anger.

Be sure your anger is under control. If you can't share your thoughts or feelings in a loving way, return to the *Time-out Process Worksheet*. If either partner's anger begins to escalate at any point during the following eight steps, return again to the *Time-out Process*.

STEP 2: Check the time.

Ask, "Is this a good time to deal with our conflict?" Depending on the intensity of the conflict, it will usually take between 10 to 45 minutes to resolve it. Very often, one partner might think it will take 10 minutes to resolve, but the other—because they have been hurt more deeply—will think 45 minutes will be needed. Therefore, be sure to give yourselves enough time to work through the following conflict resolution steps.

Note: If at the moment (due to a prior appointment or early morning work commitments, etc.,) you don't have adequate time to resolve the conflict, suggest the next best time. On occasions when it is late at night or you are exhausted, it might be best to agree upon a time the following day to resolve the issue.

STEP 3: Call on God immediately.

Couples in conflict often wait until they are totally desperate to pray. We encourage you to develop the habit of praying *before* a problem escalates, as well as during the conflict, because prayer has the power to change the entire focus of the issue as God's power and influence comes over both of you. In fact, we suggest, during this step, that you hold hands and pray out loud using the following (or similar) prayer:

> *"Lord, we love You and each other. Help us to resolve this conflict and not hurt each other. We realize that we are in a spiritual battle, so please give us Your wisdom, and understanding at this time. We're hurting; we need Your direction. Please come near to us now. Amen."*

STEP 4: Proceed with the Intentional-Empathetic Listening Worksheet.

1. Decide who will be the *Listener* and who will be the *Talker*.
2. The *Talker* begins with affirmations that are specific to the situation.
3. The *Talker* shares his or her thoughts and feelings by using "I feel" statements.
4. The *Listener* repeats what the *Talker* said and asks if they got it correct.
5. The *Listener* empathizes.
6. The *Listener* apologizes and asks for forgiveness.
7. The *Listener* asks the *Talker* if there is anything more he or she wants to share regarding this specific incident.
8. The *Talker*, if necessary, shares more "I feel" statements.
9. The *Listener* repeats the *Talker's* feelings and thoughts and then asks if he or she understood correctly. If not, the *Listener* will repeat the empathizing response (Step 5).
10. Reverse Roles. The *Talker* now becomes the *Listener* and starts with Step 2.

STEP 5: Formulate a statement that clearly identifies the conflict for both partners.

A common conflict between couples is where to spend the major holidays. If you find yourself in a similar situation, this step will help you articulate the conflict by representing each partner's feelings or desires. For example, you might say, "I want to spend Thanksgiving out of town with my family because I don't see them very often, but this is difficult for you because you feel as if your family will be alone during the holidays."

The purpose of developing this statement is to acknowledge that both of you have a reason for feeling the way you do.

STEP 6: Brainstorm possible solutions.

Share *and write down* as many solutions as possible. In this step, NO idea is a bad idea; all ideas should be freely expressed, regardless of their acceptability or feasibility. Take turns and don't interrupt each other.

Think about brainstorming from this perspective: Rather than fighting against each other, you and your partner are on one side of the table and the problem is on the opposite side of the table.

STEP 7: Agree upon a solution.

Philippians 2:2, says, "Each of you should look not only to your own interests, but also to the interests of others."

A. From your brainstorm list, decide which ideas you each would be willing to try. Be careful not to interrupt each other during this time.

B. After you agree on a solution, try to *identify any barriers* that might keep the solutions from working effectively. You must not only identify barriers, but also discuss how you will overcome them so that if/when you encounter problems, you are not tempted to believe the conflict resolution system was a waste of time.

C. Agree upon a "win-win" solution. This step usually requires that both partners compromise to some degree. If you feel resentment, you most likely haven't found the right solution. Go back to brainstorming. Do your best to find a "win-win" that feels good and right to both of you.

D. Write down the agreed upon solution. Determine the specific details, including *when* you will begin and *how* long the trial will extend. (Most solutions should be tried for a specific amount of time before becoming permanent.)

STEP 8: Try your solution and evaluate its effectiveness.

Set a time/date for re-evaluating the solution. (Example: "We agree to try the step for one month, then re-evaluate.) If this solution is not working for both of you at the end of the trial period, go back to Step 6 and brainstorm additional solutions.

Couple Assignment

Choose a recent conflict and work through each of the 8 Steps to Conflict Resolution Worksheet.

Possible Areas of Conflicts:

Driving	Automobile Purchases, Repairs, Upkeep
In-laws	Friends
Family	Opposite sex relationship
Jealousy	Fears
Spending	Politics
Church	Religion
Religious Practices	Computer
Work	Prayer
Food	Cooking
Restaurants	Sports
Shopping	Decisions
Pets	Children
Parenting	Purchases
Budgets	Vacations
Recreation	Wedding timing or planning
Honeymoon	Personality
Sexual Issues	Communication
Roles – wife, husband	Responsibilities – who does what, when, how?
Music	Movies
Entertainment	Anger Management
Addictions	Bad Habits, Annoying Behaviors
PMS	

8 Steps to Conflict Resolution Worksheet

Instructions: Be sure to go through this worksheet, step-by-step. Deal with only one incident at a time.

Step 1: Check your Anger.

Is our anger under control?	Yes / No
Can we share our thoughts/feelings in a loving way?	Yes / No
If not, does either of us need to take a time-out using the *Time-out Process*?	Yes / No

Step 2: Check the time.

Is this a good time to deal with this conflict?   Yes / No
If not, when will we resolve this problem?

_____

Step 3: Call on God immediately.

Hold hands and pray together. Ask God to help you.

Step 4: Proceed with the Intentional-Empathetic Listening Worksheet.

Who will share first (*Talker 1*)? _____

Talker 1 gives the following affirmations that are relevant to the conflict:

_____
_____

Talker 1 shares his/her thoughts and feelings about the incident:

_____
_____

Listener 1 repeats what *Talker 1* said, reflecting thoughts and feelings and showing empathy and humility. Share a time when you had the same feeling, but not when your partner did this:

_____

Listener 1 asks for forgiveness if appropriate. (Example: "I can see how I hurt you when... Will you forgive me?")

Listener asks if he/she has heard correctly and if there is anything more regarding this incident. Yes/No?

Repeat steps if necessary until you can articulate your partner's thoughts and feelings.

Reverse Roles.

Talker 2 gives the following affirmations that are relevant to the conflict:

_____

Talker 2 shares his/her thoughts and feelings regarding the incident:

_____
_____

Listener 2 repeats what Talker 2 said, reflecting thoughts and feelings and showing empathy and humility. Share a time when you had the same feeling, but not when your partner did this:

Listener 2 asks for forgiveness if appropriate. (Example: "I can see how I hurt you when... Will you forgive me?")

Listener 2 asks if he/she has heard correctly and if there is anything more regarding this incident. Yes/No?

Repeat steps if necessary until you can articulate your partner's thoughts and feelings.

Step 5: Formulate a statement that identifies the conflict clearly and encompasses both partner's feelings and desires.

_____

_____

Step 6: Brainstorm possible solutions.

1._____

2._____

3._____

4._____

5._____

Step 7: Agree upon a solution.

He is willing to try:

_____

_____

She is willing to try:

_____

_____

Barriers to his suggested solution and how we can deal with them as a couple:

_____

_____

Barriers to her suggested solution and how we can deal with them as a couple:

_____

_____

Our agreed upon solution:

_____

_____

We will begin this solution on/by:

_____

The trial period for this solution will be:

_____

Step 8: Try your Solution and Evaluate its Effectiveness

We will reevaluate this solution on (date): _____

Individual Reflection

How long did it take for you to agree upon a win-win solution? What were the most difficult steps for you? What were the most difficult steps for your partner? What did you learn from this experience that will benefit your relationship in the future?

Questions and Answers
regarding the Strategies for Managing Anger and Resolving Conflict

Q: What if you can't find a win-win solution?

A: If you cannot find a win-win solution, you may need to take a break and come back after a designated amount of time. You might also agree to meet with a mentor couple, counselor or pastor to receive non-biased insight into your situation. Be careful not to put pressure on others to tell you what to do. Ask them to help you think through some ideas neither of you may have considered. Couples almost always find a "win-win" solution if they are each willing to compromise and seek God for an answer.

Q: Some of these systems feel mechanical to me. Will it ever feel more natural?

A: If you work at it long enough, this system will feel more natural, but even if it doesn't, the benefits and outcomes will make the time and effort—and even the discomfort worth it. Even Becky and I will, on occasion, need to use one of these strategies to help us resolve a conflict. And we know we can't take short cuts. After all these years of marriage, we still have to go through them step-by-step. When we don't, we are like any couple whose anger is at risk of spinning out-of-control or escalating.

Q: What if we don't have the worksheets or books with us and we have a conflict?

A: We have developed a Pocket Edition that includes the basic communication systems in this Workbook: the 15 Rules for Effective Communication, the Intentional-Empathetic Listening Worksheet, the *Daily 5A's*, 8 Steps to Conflict Resolution, and the *Time-out Process*. We suggest that you put this "quick review" version in the glove compartment of your car, take it with you when you go on vacation or keep it in your purse or backpack. Believe it or not, couples returning from their honeymoon regret not bringing these strategies (or their Workbook) along with them.

 **5**

a biblical perspective of marriage

Seriously dating or engaged couples often remark that their relationship was "meant to be" or that God brought them together. God *does* bring couples together! Marriage is *His* design. But the tendency of many couples—at various stages—is to stop looking to God for continued direction.

God has a plan and purpose for your lives *together* as a couple. One of the greatest purposes of marriage is to bring glory to God. I Corinthian 10:31 says, *"...whatever you do, do it all for the glory of God."* To bring God glory is to put Him on display--not only for others to see Him, but be drawn to Him because of your relationship.

Therefore, it is my hope is that you would each develop a strong, personal relationship with God from this point forward in your relationship. Then, as you together explore God's perspective on relationships, and especially marriage, you will be better prepared to understand the mission He has for your lives together.

In this chapter, I provide an abundance of Bible verses that define how *"two become one," leaving and cleaving, responsibilities and roles, the power of encouragement, and spirituality in marriage* from a biblical perspective. Most importantly, as you study these verses together, you'll be very aware of your partner's beliefs, convictions, and spiritual heritage—which are very important to know about each other!

In the process of growing closer to God, you will grow closer to each other.

BIBLICAL PARTNER

The following passages describe the type of partner that God desires for us to be to one another. As you read them, underline or highlight key phrases or words that "resonate" with where you are at as a couple or where you'd like to be in the future. (Your notations will be used in the *couple assignment* at the sections end.)

A Perfect Partner:

Genesis 2:18, *The LORD God said, "It is not good for the man to be alone. I will make a helper suitable for him."*

When God made man, He did not intend for him to be alone. He made a woman for a man, so that man would not be alone. God made man and woman suitable for each other. The Greek word used for "suitable" literally means "fits like a suit." God made man and woman to fit together perfectly in many ways, especially sexually. Man and woman are two pieces of a puzzle that connect together. God designed male and female to be a couple.

A Permanent Partner:

Matthew 19:4-6, *"Haven't you read, he replied, that at the beginning the Creator made them male and female, and said, 'For this reason a man will leave his father and mother and be united to his wife, and the two will become one flesh'. So they are no longer two, but one. Therefore what God has joined together, let man not separate."*

Jesus describes the relationship between a man and woman in theses verses as "one flesh." He also implies that something mysterious takes place. When you get married, making your vows in front of family, friends and God, a mystery takes place--a miracle. God joins you together and says that no one should separate what God has joined together. Marriage, from God's perspective is permanent. Later in the passage, Jesus discusses divorce, saying that He hates it. This is a very powerful statement about God's viewpoint of marriage—He does not want anyone to make this commitment lightly or without understanding His position regarding it.

A Dependent Partner:

I Corinthians 11:11-12, *"In the Lord, however, woman is not independent of man, nor is man independent of woman. For as woman came from man, so also man is born of woman. But everything comes from God."*

Be aware. Two people becoming "one flesh" requires significant adjustment. Once you leave your parent's home as a young adult, your entire purpose is to become independent. When you decide to get married, you are, in essence, deciding to become dependent once again—this time, on your partner. Marriage is making a decision to discontinue doing only what you want to do. The couples that don't understand this biblical perspective can be tempted to believe the lie that they've made a mistake in getting married. He or she becomes susceptible to thoughts such as, "I was too young" or "I did not have enough time on my own before marrying." The truth is that everyone who marries must adjust to living dependent upon one another. It's part of the agreement.

A Loving/Respectful Partner:

Ephesians 5:31-33, *"For this reason a man will leave his father and mother and be united to his wife, and the two will become one flesh. This is a profound mystery-but I am talking about Christ and the church. However, each one of you also must love his wife as he loves himself, and the wife must respect her husband."*

Emerson Eggerich, author of ***Love and Respect***, describes this scripture as God's mandate for the husband to love his wife and the wife to respect her husband. Love results when a man loves his wife and a woman respects her husband. I would recommend this book for future marital growth.

A Sacrificial Partner:

Ephesians 5:21-23, *"Submit to one another out of reverence for Christ. Wives, submit to your husbands as to the Lord. For the husband is the head of the wife as Christ is the head of the church, his body, of which he is the Savior. Now as the church submits to Christ, so also wives should submit to their husbands in everything. Husbands, love your wives, just as Christ loved the church and gave himself up for her to make her holy, cleansing her by the washing with water through the word, and to present her to himself as a radiant church, without stain or wrinkle or any other blemish, but holy and blameless."*

This is a verse that has been misunderstood by many people. For example, it is important to note that the above scripture first instructs us to submit to one another. In my estimation, some churches or denominations overemphasize the specific role of a woman to submit to a man. While it is true that a wife is instructed to submit to her husband, it does not mean that whenever the two disagree, the wife must do what ever the husband decides. Marriage is a series of compromises and sacrifices that the husband and wife must make together. Just as Jesus submitted to His Father, we need to submit to one another in love.

 Couple Assignment

Discuss each of the previous verses—how you identified with them and share any insights you received as you read them.

 Individual Reflection

Do you feel that you and your partner have similar spiritual beliefs? If so, how will that benefit you as a person and as a couple? If not, how might that negatively impact you? Which of the verses in this section offered you a new insight into marriage? Which one of the verses do you think will be the most challenging for you to apply to your life and your relationship?

LEAVING AND CLEAVING

Genesis 2:24 (KJV) says, "Therefore shall a man leave his father and mother, and shall cleave unto his wife, and they shall be one flesh." *Leaving and cleaving*, though it might sound out-dated or old-fashioned, has great significance to every couple considering marriage. Until you leave, you cannot cleave.

Some of you will have a more difficult time leaving your parents, brothers, sisters, or friends than your partner. But in order to establish the correct attachment to your future spouse, you will need to detach from everyone else. In fact, *leaving and cleaving* may also involve a level of detachment from hobbies, work, leisure activities, or gaming.

Leaving your previous, single life is one of the first issues a couple must address. The phrase heard in many wedding vows includes, "forsaking all others." This means that couples are willing to make adjustments to *all other relationships* in order to make their partner number one priority in each other's life.

One's relationship with his or her parents may be the first relationship that needs to change. Perhaps your parents have assumed the role of your financial adviser, best friend, or confidant? When you decide to marry, your partner will need to fulfill these roles. Even friends or family members can come between you and your partner. *Leaving and cleaving* most likely will include that you will no longer communicate with past boyfriends or girlfriends. The *leaving and cleaving* principle applies to a variety of relationships. Most importantly, you and your partner must feel safe and secure with each other. Ideally, any habit, hobby, or person that can come between you and your partner must be discussed in advance of marriage, especially as accusations, jealousy, insecurity, and blaming are unacceptable ways to resolve these issues.

The following special situations will require extra sensitivity. In fact, I suggest that you follow the *8 Steps to Conflict Resolution* to discuss these issues further, and/or speak with a pastoral counselor or mentor couple to help you find win-win solutions. The goal for every premarital couple is to effectively create a "cleaving" experience for your partner. Discuss:

1. Working with your family or in a family business where daily contact is necessary.
2. Family members who may be handicapped or ill.
3. If you are divorced with children.
4. If you have a parent who is a widow or widower.
5. Cultural differences.
6. Geographical closeness to parents.
7. Parents who don't want you to leave.
8. Parents who maintain financial control.

A Leaving and Cleaving example:

Mike and Kristin had some challenges with the *leaving and cleaving* principle in the beginning of their marriage. Mike's dad had passed away seven years prior to their marriage and his mom relied heavily on Mike to help her with her finances and other household tasks. After Mike and Kristin got engaged, Kristin started having concerns about the amount of dependency Mike's mother had upon him. Whenever his mom needed anything, he would drop what he was doing to help her. Kristin could see that Mike really respected is mom and cared deeply for her welfare, however she was equally concerned about the amount of time this would take away from their relationship. They continuously struggled with the issue, which prompted them to meet with a counselor for helping in resolving this sensitive issue.

The counselor helped them find a way for Mike to help his mom without causing Kristin to feel less of a priority. Kristin also accepted the fact that because Mike's mom was a widow, their relationship with his mom would look different from their relationship with her parents. Mike also realized that he needed to continually help Kristin feel as if she was his number one priority, so he took a number of necessary action steps. First, he talked with his mom to affirm his love for her, assuring he would there for her, but that he now needed to make his new wife his first priority. Next, Kristin and Mike agreed upon a plan that included specific times Mike would be available to help his mom that worked within their schedule. The final step Mike took was to go to his brother and sister-in-law and ask if they might consider taking on a more active role in helping Mom. They were happy to get more involved. Because Mike and Kristin took the time to listen, empathize, and work within the conflict resolution system, they were able to find a lasting *win-win* solution.

Couple Assignment

Discuss the following leave and cleave *questions:*

1. What are some things/people you or your partner might need to *leave* in order to *cleave*?

2. Are there any special situations you are currently facing or might encounter in the future? If so, how will you process potential difficulties?

3. What affect will not *leaving* your parents have on your future spouse?

4. Do you know of any newlywed who has struggled to leave his or her family? What was the result?

5. Discuss in detail what your involvement with your parents will be after you are married. (Telephone contact, visitation, holidays, etc.)

Individual Reflection

What relationships or activities will most likely need to change in order for my partner to know that he or she is my number one priority? Am I prepared to make those changes?

RESPONSIBILITIES & ROLES

One of the first things couples face after they marry is the variety of responsibilities that result from sharing a home with their new spouse. Often couples will tell me that they almost feel like roommates having to decide who will do various chores such as washing dishes, laundry, dusting, yard work, automobile maintenance, paying the bills, and taking out the trash. I refer to this as the "roommate syndrome."

Couples not only struggle with *who* will do *what*, but more often they struggle with *when* and *how* these tasks will be accomplished. For example, one partner might feel that the dishes should be done immediately after dinner, while the other person would like to sit and relax before doing the dishes. There are so many things that must be done and so many different ways of doing things, that conflict is simply unavoidable. While these differences may seem petty *before you marry*, most couples will admit that they can cause considerable irritation after marriage. Talking about these responsibilities in detail before you marry helps reduce the irritation of the "roommate syndrome."

As a couple, you should take the following three areas into consideration and discuss your potential responsibilities and roles (refer to the corresponding chapters for each):

1. Personality
2. Family of origin
3. Children.

Couple Assignment

Discuss the following questions.

1. *What roles and responsibilities did you see your parents take in their marriage? How do you feel about what you observed?*

2. *Of which responsibilities and roles would you like to be held accountable in your marriage?*

3. *Which do you think you would not want to maintain? Why not?*

4. *Who do you see handling the finances in your marriage and why?*

5. *What specific things do you see the husband doing most of the time?*

6. *What specific things do you see the wife doing most of the time?*

7. *What will you do if you disagree on an important decision?*

8. *If you are blending a family, what unique differences might you experience in roles and responsibilities?*

9. If you come from different cultures, what are "his and her" responsibilities in your culture?

10. How will you handle the household and other chores? Be specific. (see list)

Grocery shopping

Pay bills

Ironing

Doing dishes

Getting children to school

Landscape work

Shopping for children

Taking care of children when sick

Car maintenance

Vacuuming and dusting

Discipline children

Taking out trash

Cooking

Helping children with homework

Washing clothes

 Individual Reflection

Based on your personality and family of origin, which responsibilities and roles will come more naturally to you? Which ones do you think you'll find more difficult? Explain.

POWER OF ENCOURAGEMENT

Philippians 4:8, "…whatever is true, whatever is noble, whatever is right, whatever is pure, whatever is lovely, whatever is admirable – if anything is excellent or praiseworthy—think about such things."

1 Thessalonians 5:11, "Therefore encourage one another and build each other up, just as in fact you are doing."

Affirmations—encouraging and loving words—are an essential aspect of a healthy relationship. One of the easiest (and free) gifts that you can give your partner is an affirmation. Affirmations allow your partner to feel loved, supported and encouraged by you.

For those who did not grow up in families where affirmations and encouragement were everyday experiences, this will be a new behavior to learn. I want you to take this exercise (and this area of your relationship) very seriously. It is easy to do and easy to learn to do. As you practice affirming each other, you'll actually begin to look forward to hearing your partner encourage and admire you with their words.

In general, very few people in your life will be as big a fan of yours as your partner—so let him or her regularly hear how much you love them and why you do.

Couple Assignment

List 15 characteristics that you love, appreciate, or admire about your partner. After you write them down, sit face to face and share them with each other. In addition, discuss how this characteristic makes you feel. (I also recommend that you make a second copy of this list and review it regularly as a visual reminder of those things that you love about your partner.)

(Example: I love that Becky is a good golfer. I especially like being recreational companions. Because we both enjoy the game of golf, we can spontaneously go hit a bucket of balls together, watch tournaments on television, or vacation near a golf course.)

1. _____
2. _____
3. _____
4. _____
5. _____
6. _____
7. _____
8. _____
9. _____
10. _____
11. _____
12. _____
13. _____
14. _____
15. _____

Individual Reflection

How difficult or enjoyable was it to hear your partner share his or her affirmations with you? Did anything surprise you? How difficult or easy do you think it will be to think of affirmations on a daily basis and share them with your partner? Is there a specific way you can be proactive or intentional in this area?

SPIRITUALITY IN YOUR MARRIAGE

Becky and I strongly believe that the spiritual area of our lives is the most important of all. We have both experienced what it feels like when God is in the center of our lives and when He was not a part of our lives. Both of us came to Christ in our twenties after much personal failure. We've learned that staying connected to God and listening to Him daily gives us the courage and ability to overcome our selfish natures and be more loving, caring, and sacrificial toward each other.

Our personal relationship with God greatly impacts every aspect of our marriage. We are convinced that no person can love us the way God does and no one can understand us like God understands us. Therefore, when we have a proper relationship with God, it puts much less stress on our relationship with our spouse. We remain focused on the knowledge that only God loves perfectly and unconditionally.

We have found a number of disciplines helpful to maintaining an intimate connection with God. Daily Bible reading, journaling our prayers, serving those in need, attending church regularly, worshipping, and giving of our tithes and offerings are many of the ways that we express our love to God. These expressions of our faith have not only increased our intimacy with God, but also with each other.

The following spiritual disciplines are important activities in developing a strong marriage.

Discuss your ideas, goals, desires, and expectations of each of them:

> Worship
> Prayer
> Bible reading
> Bible study
> Bible memory
> Small-group fellowship
> Church attendance
> Church involvement
> Service and outreach
> Tithing and giving
> Other _____

Discuss the following questions:

1. Are you willing to daily commit a specific amount of time to Bible reading and prayer? If so, how much? What would that look like?

2. As a child, what was your perception of spiritual disciplines such as Bible reading and prayer or _____? How did your parents practice these disciplines?

3. How would you like to see these spiritual disciplines implemented in your personal life, dating life, and if you marry?

4. What differences in your relationship or understanding of God do you currently possess? How do you see these differences impacting your marriage relationship?

5. Share your spiritual journey with each other from your childhood until present.

For many years, Becky and I have written our prayers in a journal as well as stayed connected to God (and each other) by daily reading the same passages from a daily Bible. We use the *Change Your Life Daily Bible*, which divides the Bible into 365 daily readings. By reading through the entire Bible each year, our knowledge and love for God grows, and so does our love and admiration for each other.

Couple Assignment

The following Bible verses and questions are additional homework for you to study, review and discuss as a couple in the coming weeks:

1. *I Corinthians 7:28 "…those who marry will face many troubles in this life, and I want to spare you this…"*

   What kind of problems do you think marriage will bring?

   Do you think most people enter marriage thinking that marriage is difficult? Why or why not? What is your perspective on this verse?

2. *I Corinthians 10:31, "… whatever you do, do it all for the glory of God."*

   How can you apply this verse to your relationship and specifically to marriage?

   What purpose do you see your marriage fulfilling, besides your own happiness?

   How will you use your marriage as a mission field?

3. *I Peter 3:7, "Husbands, in the same way be considerate as you live with your wives, and treat them with respect as the weaker partner and as heirs with you of the gracious gift of life, so that nothing will hinder your prayers".*

   How do you show respect and love to each other? Have you carefully considered that your prayers might be unanswered as a result of treating each other poorly? Discuss.

4. *Colossians 3:12-14, "Therefore, as God's chosen people, holy and dearly loved, clothe yourselves with compassion, kindness, humility, gentleness and patience. Bear with each other and forgive whatever grievances you may have against one another. Forgive as the Lord forgave you. And over all these virtues put on love, which binds them all together in perfect unity."*

   What qualities in this scripture reflect your relationship the most? What qualities in this scripture reflect your relationship the least?

Individual Reflection

Would you say that you are a devoted follower of Christ? If not, what do you think is hindering you from a committed relationship to God? What do you think you need to do or understand more clearly in order to become a follower of Christ? Do you feel that you and your partner are on the "same page" spiritually? Explain. If not, how does this make you feel?

Becky and I both came to Christ in our twenties by asking Him to come into our lives in a prayer.

If you have never asked Christ to come into your life, we encourage you to begin by professing that Jesus is God and He came to earth, was crucified on a cross, died and was buried. Three days later, He rose from the dead. He lives today and gives those who believe in Him the gift of His Holy Spirit and life eternal. (Romans 3:23, 5:8, 6:23, 10:9-10.)

If you would like to ask Him now to come into your life, we invite you to pray the following words (out-loud or silently):

> Dear Jesus,
>
> I ask you to come into my life. Forgive my sins (name anything that comes to mind). I ask you to fill me with Your Holy Spirit. Make me new and help me follow you with all of my heart. Amen.

If you've prayed this prayer, we encourage you to share this experience with a pastor, or call our office to receive more information (800-444-6189.)

There are many decisions couples need to make in their lives. What you believe about God will impact each of those decisions, especially those regarding children, church and ministry involvement, and how you spend your time and money. When couples don't share a common faith, they often experience greater conflict. The Bible uses the phrase "unequally yoked" to describe the union between a believer and a non-believer (II Corinthians 6:14.) God's warns us in this matter because He loves us and wants what is best for us. We encourage you to meet with a pastor if you are in an "unequally yoked" relationship.

NOTES

 **6**

sexual intimacy

Great marriages just don't happen naturally. Throughout this workbook we have emphasized that marriage is a relationship that takes intention and effort. The same is true with sex. Married couples need both knowledge and skills in order to have a satisfying sexually intimate relationship.

Great sex just doesn't happen naturally either. According to a recent sex survey over 50 percent of couples said they were "less than satisfied" with their sexual intimacy. One of every four women never or rarely experience orgasm and it is not uncommon for intercourse to be painful.[1]

I've taught the principles of sexual intimacy to premarital couples for many years and I've found that authors, Cliff and Joyce Penner provide the most concise and practical information. Much of the material in this chapter comes from what I have learned from the Penners and would recommend many of their resources, especially *Getting Your Sex Life Off to a Great Start*[2] (even to take on your honeymoon.)

Let's start by discussing sex after marriage.

SEX AFTER MARRIAGE

Sexual Goals:
The primary goal in your sexual relationship should be to please your partner, not necessarily to reach orgasm together. If reaching orgasm is your goal, your intimacy will be performance based. If you make it your goal to touch your partner in ways that please him or her, both performance pressure and fear of failure will be minimized and you'll be much more likely to enjoy each sexual experience.

Sexual Passion:
Most husbands will need to slow down when it comes to sex, especially on the honeymoon! Often he is so excited that he moves too quickly through the initial stages of lovemaking. In most cases, it takes approximately ten times longer for a woman to get to the same place as a man (example: if he is ready in two minutes, it might take her twenty minutes.) I often jokingly say to my class, "Women are like computers, they need to be plugged in, booted up, logged onto, programmed and they need a password. Men are like microwave ovens turn them on, hit the button and they are ready to go."

Sexual Initiation:

Wives need to learn to be more comfortable taking the lead in their sexual relationship. Husbands become frustrated when they have to initiate sex most of the time. Initiating doesn't feel natural for the wife because she might not have the same, quickly-aroused feelings as her husband. But if you allow your feelings to dictate your sex life, you will most likely not achieve the satisfaction you desire. As I have previously discussed in this workbook, couples need to become consistently intentional with every aspect of their relationship, moving away from doing things only if they come naturally.

Sexual Conversation:

Communication is very important during the sexual experience. You may initially be embarrassed to talk about sex, but as you each communicate about your experience with your partner, you will both receive the benefits of a satisfying sex life. Communicating with your spouse is a learning experience where you let each other know both what feels good and what does not feel good. Sometimes you might communicate verbally; at other times you might be more comfortable communicating nonverbally. Either way, I encourage you to lovingly convey your sexual desires with your spouse by directing him or her to places on your body—and in a manner—that feel satisfying to you. Be sure to speak gently to your partner about your sexual experience, never criticizing him or her in this area of your relationship. If you *don't* enjoy something, let your partner know this in a very loving way. For example, you can say, "That feels good when you touch me in this way, but it is less enjoyable when you touch me in this way." It is important to discuss any specific aspect of sex that you don't enjoy. In fact, it is very common to have different sexual preferences. Be sure to talk to your spouse about your preferences in advance of lovemaking. Finally, pressuring your partner to have sex or to perform in a way that they find offensive will hurt your relationship. Being other-focused and selfless are integral characteristics to enjoying a sexually intimate relationship.

Sexual Preferences:

There is no right or wrong preference when it comes to the frequency of sex within your marriage, but it can become another area of conflict for many couples if you don't talk about it. Some couples make love once a month; others enjoy making love every day. The important issue is what works for both of you. Seventy percent of couples make love between one to three times per week.[3]

Sexual Difficulties:

If you are experiencing problems in your sexual relationship, don't wait long before seeking help. If you are experiencing difficulties (such as, painful penetration, inability to sustain an erection, etc.) after a few weeks of marriage, I suggest that you seek counseling. Don't wait or be embarrassed. It is common for over 50% of couples struggle in this area. I strongly suggest that you take the book, **Restoring the Pleasure**, by Cliff and Joyce Penner, on your honeymoon!

Sexual Abuse:

If you have experienced sexual abuse in your past, I recommend that you meet with a counselor as a couple. Usually this type of trauma needs special attention.

SEX BEFORE MARRIAGE

There are many facets to sexual intimacy. The discovery of each other's physical bodies, deciding upon sexual frequency and preferences, and perhaps dealing with pain or premature ejaculation are just a few of the many elements of the sexual experience. Therefore, I strongly (and repeatedly) encourage *all* of my couples to purchase the Penner's book, ***Getting Your Sex Life Off to a Great Start***, as it both clinically and practically addresses these and other important sexual intimacy issues.

I encourage you—for many reasons—to abstain from sex before you marry.

The Protection of Sexual Intimacy within Marriage:

When the Bible says, "two shall become one," it suggests that sex unites us in a mysterious and sacred way as we become one flesh. This is not merely a physical experience; it is also a very powerful spiritual experience. When you give your body to someone sexually, you are also giving them your soul and your spirit. God's design for sex is reserved for marriage. Because the sexual union is so powerful—allowing the most private parts of your physical body to be experienced by another person—God wants both the man and woman to be protected by the covenant of marriage.

The Problems of Cohabitation:

In today's culture, it is both popular for couples to live together before marriage, as well as be sexually active before the wedding. Some couples reason that they must live together to see if they are compatible; others suggest they are cohabitating to save money.

Proverbs 14:12 says, "There is a way that seems right to man, but in the end it leads to death." In the Old Testament book, Judges 21:25 (NAS), when Israel was about to be judged by God for committing great sins, the author wrote, "…everyone did what was right in his own eyes." People often do what *they* think is right, paying little or no attention to God's ways. This is a pattern that will lead to destruction. If you choose to do what is right in your own eyes and do not allow God to direct you, you will most likely hurt your relationship both now and in the future.

In a study of the sexual practices among couples, the most satisfied with their sex lives were married couples who believed that sex should be saved for marriage. Cohabitating couples studied were less satisfied relationally and 50% more likely to break up than married couples.[4]

Sex is Not Just Intercourse

Unmarried couples often suggest that as long as they are not having sexual intercourse, they are not having sex. But sexual intimacy is not just about intercourse. It involves any activities, thoughts, and body parts that arouse sexual feeling.

I Corinthians 6:1 says, "Flee from sexual immorality. All other sins a man commits are outside his body, but he who sins sexually sins against his own body." Sexual sins can be easy to rationalize. Here are some rationalizations you may have been tempted to use: (As you read them, ask yourself if any of them sound familiar.)

"But we love each other."

"We are going to be married soon."

"It's like we are already married."

"We're not teenagers."

"I just want a back rub."   (Back rubs can quickly turn into front rubs.)

"If they went this far with someone else, I deserve to go this far with my partner."

"How will we know we are compatible if we don't have sex?"

"We'll be able to stop ourselves."

"I wouldn't buy a car without a test drive."

"What do you expect, I'm not Jesus."

"God will understand."

"Since we aren't perfect, we may as well do it anyway."

"Since we have gone this far already, we might as well keep going."

Interestingly, people don't use these same rationalizations in other areas. For example, if you were to cut off the end of your finger, you wouldn't say, "Since I've gone this far, I may as well cut off my whole finger."

Sexual passion will test your character, especially your selfishness factor. Most of us want what we want when we want it. Therefore, our willingness to set aside our sexual desires or to sacrifice our desires out of obedience toward God and respect for our partner will test our level of self-control and spiritual maturity. But refraining from sexual intimacy until marriage demonstrates respect, love and humility to your partner, as well as to God.

Most importantly, if you are not able to exhibit unselfishness and self-control in this area before marriage, you are establishing a pattern of unwillingness to obey God and respect boundaries after marriage.

Touching and Looking Arouses and Awakens

A poetic book in the Bible, the Song of Solomon, discusses sexual intimacy from a premarital perspective. Three separate times in the Song of Solomon (2:7, 3:5, and 8:4) this statement is repeated, "Do not arouse or awaken love until it so desires." This is just one more passage in the Bible that clearly instructs couples to wait until marriage to arouse sexual desire.

Many couples set boundaries but repeatedly *arouse and awaken* sexual desires, rationalizing that they will be able to contain them after arousal has begun. Proverbs 22:3 (NAS) says, "A man sees danger and proceeds anyway." In the area of sexual intimacy, couples all too often proceed anyway, but are inevitably chased by guilt and shame.

As an elementary school guidance counselor, it came to my attention that some of the students were going to the bathroom and touching each other's private parts. So the principal asked me to speak to them about inappropriate sexuality. I taught them the basics of sexuality by showing them a diagram of their sexual organs and then telling them that those were their "private parts." I concluded my little sessions with the statement, "Don't look at or touch each other's private parts." Afterward, when I would see the children in the halls, they would proudly come up to me and say, "We aren't touching our private parts anymore!" I would smile and encourage them.

I later became a junior high school counselor and ended up having the same conversation with 7th and 8th graders. I kept the same line, "Don't look at or touch each other's private parts." Next, I became a high school counselor and (as you probably might guess) used the same statement with them: "Don't look at or touch each other's private parts."

When I moved to college ministry, it was my college students who heard this story but asked, "You aren't going to tell us the same thing, are you?" I responded, "When the Bible says, 'Don't awaken love until it is the time,' I believe it is referring to those situations and relationships that are not within marriage. So yes, I am going to ask you not to look at or touch each other's private parts until you get married."

Now I am a premarital pastor and couples tell me that they are getting married very soon, so perhaps they should not have to follow the same parameters. I tell them I am excited for them because they don't have to wait much longer, but I still suggest, "Don't look at or touch each other's private parts until you are married. But when you get married—look and touch!"

My suggestion for you, so that you won't arouse or awaken love until it is time: *Do not look at or touch each other's private parts.*

Setting Premarital Boundaries

As a pastor and counselor, I cannot think of one area in which it would be more important for you to set boundaries than in the sexual area of your relationship. In fact, because this is such a difficult area in which to maintain discipline, I also encourage you to discuss your boundaries with a mentor or accountability partner.

For many couples, this might require a dramatic change in your current level of intimacy. Some of you will have to stop living together. Others of you will need to stop laying down next to each other. Many of you will have to make a decision to stop spending the night together. But please, make a decision, first to hear God's voice on this issue and then obey Him. Show your love for God and respect for the covenant of marriage by remaining sexually pure.

I also believe that God wants to give you a new start in this area today.

Whether or not you have crossed your and/or God's boundaries, I encourage you to make a fresh commitment to purity. Don't buy the lie that you have gone too far or it's too late to start over. I have seen many couples recommit to sexual purity after they had gone well beyond their boundaries, successfully abstaining from sexual intimacy until their wedding night. They also found this experience to provide a cleansing and renewal in their relationship with God. Most excitedly, they walked down the aisle on their wedding day prepared to give themselves in a passionate and renewed way to their spouse.

If you do need a fresh start in this area with each other, begin by asking God to forgive you for your past. Let the following prayer lead you:

Lord, please forgive us. Help us start fresh today. Help us to find and share with our accountability partners what boundaries You desire for us to keep in this area. Help us not even show a hint of sexual immorality, nor the appearance of evil. We commit to sexual purity in our relationship. Thank you for forgiving us and giving us a new start.

I encourage you to set sexual boundaries early in your relationship. It is important that you do this in the "cool" of the day, not in the "heat" of romantic or sexual feelings. In addition, honor your partner's desires for purity and do not compromise your standards by putting yourselves in places that would put your purity agreement at risk. Discuss the areas that will put you in compromising situations. Please consider making the following Purity Agreement with your partner at this time, and then ask an accountability couple to both sign your agreement and help you remain true to your desire and commitment. Give them permission to regularly ask if you are being true to your commitment.

Purity Agreement

Hebrews 13:4 (The Message,) "Honor marriage, and guard the sacredness of sexual intimacy between wife and husband."

I Corinthians 6:18, "Flee from sexual immorality. All other sins a man commits are outside his body, but he who sins sexually sins against his own body."

Ephesians 5:3, "But among you there must not be even a hint of sexual immorality, or of any kind of impurity, or of greed, because these are improper for God's holy people."

We have established our boundaries to be:

_____

_____

_____

We desire to honor God and our partner by remaining sexually pure. Whether we have remained pure or not up to this time, we decide today to wait until marriage to be sexually intimate. We make this commitment to God and each other.

Signed _____   Signed _____

Witness_____   Witness_____

We make this Purity Agreement on_____ (date).

PRAYER FOR FORGIVENESS, HEALING AND FREEDOM FROM PREVIOUS RELATIONSHIPS AND SEXUAL SINS

Many couples enter relationships with a sexual past. Their past can negatively impact their future dating or marriage relationships. Therefore I suggest that in addition to seeing a counselor for any unresolved or recurring issues, you would pray the following prayer. Many who have prayed this prayer often express how they have experienced a new release or freedom. You can pray this prayer for forgiveness and healing alone or with a pastor or mentor (not with your partner).

The Prayer:

Dear Heavenly Father,

I confess that I have sinned against you by participating in sexual behaviors that have not been within your perfect will for my life. I ask you to forgive me for my part in these events. Please break all physical, sexual, spiritual and soul ties I have made with past sexual partners or objects. I forgive anyone who was involved in any aspects of these past sins.

Deliver, cleanse, and heal me from evil. Please heal the memories in me and in those who were a part of this sinful behavior. (Take a few minutes right now to silently name the events and people.) Please remove any influence they may have over me. I renounce my involvement in any practices that were sinful.

Father, take away any evil spirits from me and cancel any rights they might have had over me.

May the blood of Christ cleanse me, renew me, return me to wholeness, and cancel any of the consequences and ties that are over me or could result from these events or people. I claim my full deliverance, healing and forgiveness in the name of Jesus Christ.

Thank you for forgiving, healing, delivering, and breaking these ties over me. I accept your sacrifice on the cross as the payment for my sins. You are my Lord and Savior. I give you my entire being, my spirit, soul and body as a living sacrifice. I ask you to totally fill me with your Holy Spirit that I might live the Christian life in a way that pleases you. I ask that your power working in me will guard my heart and mind.

I commit to rejecting any temptations to dwell on those experiences that would reconnect me emotionally, spiritually, physically or mentally to my past in any way. Please give me wisdom and a discerning spirit to recognize these temptations. I commit my life to you, Lord, and thank you for providing me with forgiveness, deliverance, healing and wholeness.

In the name of Jesus, my Lord and Savior.

Amen.

1. *Talk with your partner and consider signing the* **Purity Agreement** *in this workbook.*

2. *Purchase* **Getting Your Sex Life Off to a Great Start** *by Cliff and Joyce Penner.*

3. *Discuss the following 16 questions.*

I strongly suggest you discuss these questions at a time when you will not be tempted to be sexually intimate. I also suggest you commit to sexual purity before you read these questions. If you are in an early stage of dating, I do not recommend that you discuss these questions until you are closer to engagement or already engaged. In addition, please let your mentor, pastor, or counselor/ accountability partner know that you are discussing these questions.

While it may be difficult to answer some of these accurately, it is important that you at least consider them and share some ideas of what you think your response would be.

1. *Do you have any fears regarding sexual intimacy with your future spouse? If so what are they?*

2. *What will you do when your partner is not interested in being intimate at the time you are interested?*

3. *How many times do you think you will have sexual intercourse each week? How many times do you think your spouse will want to have sex each week? How will you deal with your differences, if you have them?*

4. *Are there any sexual activities, positions, and ways of touching or satisfying each other that you would rather not practice?*

5. *What do you feel will be the best "love-making" positions? How would you feel about trying different positions?*

6. *Do you feel it is acceptable to satisfy each other without sexual intercourse?*

7. *Will you go for counseling if you have difficulty achieving sexual satisfaction? How long will you wait before seeing a counselor?*

8. *Will it feel like failure if you or your partner does not climax during sexual intercourse?*

9. *If you are going to use birth control, what method or methods will you use? Who will be responsible to take care of this matter?*

10. *How do you feel about making love with the lights on, low, or off?*

11. *Do you think you can respect your partner if they do not want to be involved in a specific sexual activity such as oral sex? How will you resolve the difference?*

12. Are there any areas regarding sex that bother or confuse you?

13. Can you share any ideas that might help you have a better sex life?

14. Are there any sexual identity issues for which you need answers before getting married?

15. Is there anything from your past that might affect your sex life? Explain.

16. Would you be willing to go to the doctor for examination and blood tests before we marry? (I highly recommend this.)

Individual Reflection

What is your attitude about sex? What experiences from your past influence your feelings or thoughts about sex? What are some of the ideas that you believe about sex, such as: "sex is..." good, bad, dirty, or beautiful? Do you feel you have sexual temptation under control? If not, what steps will you to take to overcome theses temptations? Are you willing to sign the Purity Agreement? If not what could be hindering you?

1 Scott Floyd, *"Newlyweds and Sex: What's Going on for Christian Couples?"* <u>Marriage and Family: A Christian Journal</u> 7 2004: 104-106.

2 Clifford and Joyce Penner, <u>Getting Your Sex Life Off to a Great Start</u> (Carol Stream, IL: W Publishing Group, 1994).

3 Floyd 103.

4 David Gudgel, <u>Before You Life Together</u> (Ventura, CA: Regal Publishers, 2003) 40.

NOTES...

....

....

....

....

....

....

....

....

....

....

....

....

....

....

....

 **7**

parenting

PREPARING FOR PARENTING

Parenting is one of the most difficult but most rewarding privileges you can experience in life. It also is a unique challenge of which many people find themselves ill-equipped. Often during premarital preparation, couples don't spend a lot of time thinking about parenting because it can seem so far off into the future and not a priority issue. It may seem like trying to plan how you will tackle a new task at work before you've been given the position. This workbook provides limited input on parenting, so we strongly suggest you begin to read more on this topic and attend parent-education classes when you decide to begin a family. Classes will provide information that will better equip you and your partner for this lifelong responsibility.

Parenting will most certainly change your marriage; bringing both joys and challenges to you as a couple. The tools you are learning in this book will perhaps be even more important when children enter the scene. One couple had to use *Conflict Resolution* more times in the first 6 months of parenting than they did the entire first 2-years of marriage. Children are a wonderful blessing but the physical, emotional and spiritual responsibility may also bring additional pressure on a marriage. Thus, we strongly recommend you practice the skills you have been learning and get into the discipline of using them in your early years of marriage. One reason why the *Daily 5 A's* is such an important tool is because after years of marriage and the responsibility of kids, it becomes very easy for your marriage to become a business relationship. Managing the house, carpooling the kids, paying bills, etc., can make your relationship seem robotic. If not carefully tended after, the marriage can seem more like a roommate relationship. More than ever, you need a time at the end of the day to connect emotionally and physically. When asked about the *Daily 5 A's*, one woman said that after her husband asked her if he did anything that day to hurt her, she responded, "I didn't even see or talk to you today so how could you have hurt me?" It seems slightly humorous and yet is a good example of why this daily discipline is so important after you have kids.

If you apply many of the skills you have learned through this book to parenting, being a parent will become much easier. For example, the empathetic connection will increase your effectiveness as a parent. Research has proven the parent's capacity to be empathetic increases their ability to nurture their children, protect them from risk and enhance their developmental experiences.[1] Some couples use Intentional-Empathetic Listening with their young children to make sure they understand what their kids are saying before making assumptions and disciplining. The Intentional-Empathetic Listening system is especially helpful with teenagers who often complain that their parents don't understand them. Another couple uses a modified form of the *Daily 5 A's* to affirm, apologize, and pray for their kids every night.

Ultimately, the most wonderful gift you can give your children is the example of a loving marriage. Your marriage will set the precedence for how your children will relate with their friends and their future spouse. They will emulate what they see you model at home. So the investment you make to ensure a strong marriage will not only impact you but will impact your children, grandchildren and generations to come.

I believe one of the most important things you can do before you marry is to talk to each other about how you and your siblings were parented. Share some of what you would like to continue with your children and what you would try to change. Following are some questions that can guide you through this experience.

Questions Regarding Parenting:

1. How much TV do you feel is acceptable for children to watch?

2. What are the acceptable and unacceptable forms of discipline for our children? At what ages will these guidelines change?

3. Who will discipline the children? Will we have different roles in discipline?

4. How will we handle money with our children? Will we expect them to work for their allowance? At what ages? What chores will be required of them and at what ages?

5. What will our parents' roles be as grandparents of our children? What problems do we anticipate? Will we allow them to discipline the children? How will we handle our parents giving us advice about raising children, especially if it's different than what we've decided we want to do?

6. Will we send our children to private schools, religious schools or teach them from home?

7. Will we raise them in the church? What will we expect their involvement to be?

8. How involved should they be in sports, music, foreign language, etc.? At what age would we like to see them developing in these areas? How much time spent in extra-curricular activities would be considered too much? How do we prioritize these activities with family, church, school/homework, etc.?

9. How will we handle the children when they want to come into our bedroom? Will they sleep with us and for how long?

10. Are we similar in our perspectives on how to handle a crying infant? Will we allow them to cry or will we pick them up immediately?

11. What is our policy on junk food? How important is nutrition and sleep to each of us?

12. Will we purchase a car for our children when they are old enough to drive?

13. What will our policy be on movies and video games?

14. What will our policy be on curfews?

15. How will we ensure our children see us as unified in our expectations, answers and discipline?

STEP PARENTING

While step-parenting can be a very special and unique experience, it will also bring on some very new and distinct issues. Whether after divorce or loss of a loved one, couples who find themselves in a new love relationship can be blind to the fact that in every new relationship there will be challenging situations. Some of the issues that need to be addressed include the ex-spouse's involvement with the children and with you, specific relational boundaries, discipline, acceptance of children, and acceptance of step-parents. We have a list of questions that we highly recommend you thoroughly discuss. Think about each of the possibilities, and consider interviewing other married couples and step-parents. Be aware that child rearing is one of the top three areas of conflict in marriage, so be prepared with additional readings and study.

Questions Unique to Step Parenting:

1. How will we deal with ex-spouse's roles in parenting?

2. How will you communicate with your ex-spouse? With what frequency will you email, write letters, make phone calls?

3. How will you work through conflicts with ex-spouses and children?

4. In what way will we plan holidays and with whom?

5. What unique roles will we take as step-parents? Regarding discipline, what roles will we take?

6. Sometimes in the beginning of the remarriage, children are excited about the new family, but resentment sets in when difficulties occur. How will you handle these situations?

7. Where will we go for help if we begin to have difficulties with blending our families? How soon will we seek it?

8. How will we deal with the dedication we each have to our biological children? How will we deal with the temptation to feel the other is putting their child's priorities above others?

9. If we desire to have a child together, how will we ensure that our biological children and step-children do not feel they are less of a priority?

10. What financial problems do we anticipate? How will we deal with them?

 Couple Assignment

... for couples who are not blending families.

Interview 4 couples you respect, who have from 1 to 5 children. Ask them what their greatest joy and struggle has been in parenting. What advice would they give you for starting a family? What advice would they give you before marrying to prepare yourselves for parenting?

Couple Assignment

...for couples who are considering blending families

1. Answer both of the previous sections: Questions Regarding Parenting, *and the* Additional Questions Unique to Step-Parenting. *Look in the Additional Resources section in the back of this workbook and identify any books you might want to use as additional readings in this area.*

2. Interview 4 individuals or couples who are in blended families or have been in step-families. Ask them the following questions:

1. *Can you share what the blessings of blending your family have been?*

2. *What have you learned from your experiences?*

3. *What was surprising to you after you got married?*

4. *What resources have you found helpful in step-parenting?*

5. *What skills do you think we will need to effectively deal with our unique situation?*

6. *Have holidays or child custody been difficult? If so, can you share how and what we might do to prepare for these issues?*

7. *Have you experienced any problems with the children's adjustment?*

8. *Have you encountered any legal or financial issues? Do you have any advice to offer us regarding these areas?*

 Individual Reflection

What insights have you gained by processing the questions and interviewing the couples from your assignment? Have your attitudes changed on any issues of parenting or step-parenting? What additional help will you need?

---

1 K. Kilpatrick, *"The Parent Empathy Project,"* <u>NSW Department of Community Services</u>, Glebe 30 (2004): 1.

 **8**

next steps

Over a thousand couples have gone through the material in *Seriously Dating or Engaged*, but a young couple recently wrote to me, capturing the essence of what I hope every couple will experience. Not only did the practical systems improve their relationship before marriage, but also after marriage they have continued to grow by using the Worksheets and accepting the challenge I extend to all my couples—to acquire a mentor couple.

An *Open Letter* from a young couple...

> David and I met a few years ago while working at Disneyland. We had a pretty "normal" dating experience. Along with our "normal" dating experience, we had our "normal" share of disagreements, arguments, temporary break-ups, etc. But once we got engaged, we realized that we needed to grow up and take responsibility for the commitment we were about to make to each other, our families and friends, and to God. This is when we started going to **ROCK**HARBOR.
>
> We come from very different yet similar family backgrounds. David was raised in a Methodist household and I in a Catholic one. A lot of our struggles came from our differences in our religious upbringing. We started coming to **ROCK**HARBOR because it was neutral ground—a place we could start off together. One day the pre-marriage counseling class was flashed up on the screen and I nudged David and said, "Hey, you want to do that?" He said yes and so we signed up.
>
> For us, when we signed up for the class, it was more like another thing that was on the "Before the Wedding" check list—somewhere between picking out a dress and deciding on a cake. We had no idea how much it would impact our relationship. Thru this class we learned about ourselves as individuals and how that works as a couple. I learned why David always forgets where his wallet is and why I feel like I have to share my opinions about everything with everyone.
>
> We also learned how to manage our conflicts—shockingly, no more fighting and slamming the door and walking out turned out not to be the most constructive way to disagree! Now we have a safe space to manage our conflicts. We also work on our relationship every single day and make that commitment to each other to do so. By doing this, we solve small problems before they pile up and become issues. The difference this makes in our relationship is amazing.
>
> We also took a look at our faith and our religions. Our faiths and beliefs were the same;

our ways of practicing and worshipping were and still are different in many ways. But our religious conflict was no longer about one person trying to convert the other but to how we can take our shared beliefs and move forward. This has brought us into a closer relationship with each other and with God.

After the class, we went and had a fabulous wedding in Costa Rica and returned to our new lives together. But our instruction isn't over yet. We have been paired with a couple who became our marriage mentors and who will stay with us thru the first two years of our lives together. They help to point out potential stumbling blocks ahead and to learn from what we have been thru. It's like having a GPS system for our marriage—they know where we are going and what we will be going thru and the countless different ways to get there.

Now we are two years into our marriage and the commitment we made to each other when we started down this path is stronger every day. The people we were when we got engaged really had no idea what we were getting ourselves into. Marriage just seemed like fun - we loved each other and that's all you need, right? We were so wrong. We have seen too many of our friends and family members lose their marriages and we do not want to lose what we have—ever.

Perhaps to some, this premarital material, meeting with our marriage mentors, and our daily 5 A's may seem a bit much. But to us, when you have made a commitment to God and to another person that will last a lifetime and more, wouldn't you want to do everything in your power to make it the best it can be?

RED FLAGS AND WARNINGS:

Proverbs 22:3 (NAS) says, "A fool sees danger and proceeds anyway."

Over the years, as a counselor and pastor, I've met with many unhappy couples. They unfortunately transitioned from excitement and hope to disillusionment and despair, primarily because they didn't heed the red flags and warning signs.

Before your premarital instruction is complete, I want you to individually reflect on each of the following statements, then discuss your answers with your partner and *don't* be afraid to ask the hard questions *now* (and not later.)

> Does your partner abuse drugs, alcohol or other substances?
>
> Do they hide things or are they secretive?
>
> Do they have problems with money? Are they in debt?
>
> Do they have unhealthy eating patterns?
>
> Are there any signs of pornography?

Do they have any habits you can't live with or handle?

Are your partner's friends people with whom you would have a difficult time being friends?

Does your partner treat his or her parents, family, and friends in an unhealthy way?

Do you have trouble trusting your partner?

Does your partner have a difficult time making or keeping commitments?

When you have a disagreement or argument, does your partner refuse to talk or explode?

Does your partner make you jealous?

Has your partner been unfaithful to you?

Do you have thoughts like, "What it would be like to marry someone else?"

Do you and your partner have few things in common?

Does your partner have different religious beliefs than you?

If you are seriously dating, and either of you answered yes to any of the previous questions, I strongly recommend that you both meet with a counselor or pastor. If you are already engaged and answered yes to any of the questions that would make it difficult to live with your fiancé for the rest of your life, you should highly consider delaying your wedding. Even a *yes* answer to only one of the previous questions could significantly hurt your chances of having a successful marriage.

The Benefit of a Mentor Couple:

Research suggests that the first twenty-four months of marriage is a critical time for couples to establish their marital bond.[1] Therefore, I suggest that all of my premarital couples meet with a mentor couple at least every quarter for the first two years of marriage.

Remember, the role of a mentor couple is to serve as supportive friends that encourage, support and pray for you, more than to act as your counselors.

The role of the mentor couple before you marry:

1. Answer questions you may encounter when going through the Workbook.

2. Check on your assignments and reflections from each chapter.

3. Help you get connected to other resources, such as church groups, pastoral help or counselors.

4. Take you through the PREPARE Inventory, if they have been trained to do so. If they are not trained, they can contact our office for our next Prepare Training Workshop or the Prepare-Enrich website (http://www.prepare-enrich.com) to find a trained counselor or pastor who could assist you.

The role of the mentor couple after you marry:

1. Ongoing support and encouragement after you marry.

2. Answer questions you may encounter in adjusting to marriage (or help you find the answers).

3. Help you stay accountable to the *Daily 5A's*, the *8 Steps to Conflict Resolution*, etc.

4. Assist you in finding other marriage enrichment experiences in order to grow stronger in your commitment to each other.

Questions a mentor couple should ask you after you marry:

1. What do you feel is going well in your marriage?

2. What are you learning about marriage?

3. What does the "roommate syndrome" look like in your relationship?

4. Are you doing your *Daily 5 A's* regularly? Are they helping you connect with each other in three to five minutes each day? If not, how can we help you get back on track?

5. Are you using the *Intentional-Empathetic Listening* and *8 Steps to Conflict Resolution* Worksheets? Are there any recurring issues that require you use them?

6. How is your spiritual life? (Discuss your prayer life, Bible reading, church attendance and church involvement.)

7. Are there any areas in which you are struggling?

8. How would you rate your adjustment to the following issues...?

   Household roles and management
   Relationships with family and friends
   Communication
   Leisure activities
   Sexual adjustments
   Financial adjustments
   Spirituality as a couple
   Occupation

9. Is there any way they could help you in your marriage?

10. How can they pray for you as a couple?

TAKING THE PREPARE INVENTORY BEFORE YOU MARRY

I encourage all my couples to supplement their premarital reading and assignments by taking a premarital inventory called the PREPARE Inventory. This inventory of approximately 160 questions is designed to help you explore your strengths and growth areas, giving you a thorough opportunity to learn more about your partner and assess your relationship.

More and more pastors are trained to administer and interpret the results, but if you can't find someone in your area, contact our office for our next training course or contact Prepare-Enrich directly at http://www.prepare-enrich.com and they will assist you.

Final words of encouragement...

From a mentor couple...

"We have been privileged to walk alongside many engaged and newlywed couples, mentoring and challenging them to use the "tools" presented in this book. *Not only have we witnessed significant improvements in their relationships, we have also come to a deeper understanding of one another and experienced greater marital satisfaction in our own relationship.* In fact, our communication skills have been taken to a higher level."

—Denny & Sue Bourgeois, Mentor Couple, Married 30 years

From a newlywed Couple...

"Before we got married, this material gave us tools to manage our expectations appropriately and discuss difficult issues. Now that we're married, we know how to use these tools, *and because we have agreed to use them*, we don't need to hide our feelings or opinions in fear of starting an argument. We know we can compromise and create attractive win-win solutions together. They've given us the keys to an honest, open, and authentic relationship.

We've heard people say that the first year of marriage is the most difficult, but we couldn't disagree more. The premarital material and training we received from Roger made our first year of marriage our best year together!"

—Peter and Katie Oakman, Huntington Beach, California

Closing prayer and word from Roger and Becky

We pray that your relationship would be transparent and honest, built on biblical principles, and strengthened by daily spiritual and relational disciplines. We ask the Lord to give you the courage to be a reflection of His love to your family and friends. We pray that you would look for His guidance and wisdom daily by listening to His voice. Amen.

---

1 Ted L. Huston, et al., *"The Connubial Crucible: Newlywed Years as Predictors of Marital Delight, Distress, and Divorce,"* Journal of Personality and Social Psychology, 2001; 80: 237.

NOTES...

....

....

....

....

....

....

....

....

....

....

....

....

....

....

....

....

leader's guide

Seriously Dating or Engaged: A Premarital Workbook

As a pastor, mentor, or therapist working with couples, you are making a significant investment in a seriously dating or engaged couples' relationship. Statistics reveal that a high-quality premarital program can significantly increase a couple's chances of having a satisfying marriage.[1] In fact, a 10-year study using Prepare/Enrich, a premarital program using a couple assessment inventory with a four to eight week feedback session, produced a divorce rate of only 2% of those who participated. Compared with the national divorce rate of about 40%, the importance of marriage preparation is undeniable.[2] Research also suggests that the first two years are critical for a couple's bonding.[3] Being mentored during the early stages of marriage is extremely important as research has shown that couples who divorced within the first two years of marriage experienced disillusionment in the first few months of marriage.

In the course of developing my premarital materials, I felt it was equally important to design a follow-up mentor program that suggested a two-year commitment for the mentors and mentees. In recruiting mentor couples, I suggest that you need not have a perfect marriage, but a good one. Because every marriage struggles in some way, it would be disingenuous to suggest a 'perfect' marriage would be possible to achieve. In fact, some of the most significant comfort a mentor couple will provide to a young couple may be to humbly share some of your past struggles or weaknesses.

This **Leader's Guide** is designed to help you facilitate meetings with your premarital couple. Each chapter in *Seriously Dating or Engaged: A Premarital Workbook* gives the couple information on a particular topic, provides a Couple Assignment and Individual Reflection. It works best for couples to share their assignments and reflections with you during your meetings. If you are facilitating a larger group, (up to 200 is possible) divide couples into smaller groups, each with a co-leader. (I have found that 10 to 15 hours is needed to adequately present the material in this Workbook. The group classes I teach are for four weeks on Saturday mornings from 9:00 am to 12:30 pm.)

LEADERS GUIDE
FOR WORKING WITH COUPLES ONE-ON-ONE:

Whether you are a pastor, counselor or therapist, you are entering into a mentoring **One-on-One** relationship where you will have the privilege to encourage and support a younger couple. If you work with a couple before they marry, you will assign them readings from the Workbook and then follow through with them each week by checking on their Couple Assignments and Individual Reflections. (*This material can be adapted for as few as seven sessions or up to twelve sessions.*)

My hope is not only that you will make a significant difference in the lives and relationship of your couple, but that your marriage will also be deeply enriched by this experience.

LEADERS GUIDE

Session 1.

❑ During the first meeting ask the couple how and when they met, what attracted them to each other and to describe their spiritual journey.

❑ Share a little about your life. Tell them about the length of your marriage, how you met, your current family, etc. If you had premarital preparation, explain what it was like for you. If you didn't have an opportunity, tell them that you are proud that they are taking great efforts to make their future marital relationship a quality, God-centered priority.

❑ Introduce them to the *Seriously Dating or Engaged: A Premarital Workbook* and begin Chapter One: **Communicating Effectively**. Go through the *15 Rules* in detail, *Feeling Words*, *Intentional-Empathetic Listening* and *Daily 5 A's*. Ask them to do any assignments from the "Assignments" section in their Workbooks. Ask them to do the *Daily 5 A's* (Affirmation, Affection, Apology, Ask, and Amen) for one week. Have them take the *CORE Personality Inventory* found in Chapter 3. (It is very important that they take it before they come to the next meeting because you will be going through the results with them). Let them know that each meeting will include a time of accountability for each of the assignments.

❑ Before your next meeting with the couple, familiarize yourself with their assignments by practicing the *Daily 5 A's* (p. 15), as well as taking and scoring the **CORE Personality Inventory** (pages 29-30).

Session 2.

❑ Have them share their assignments from Chapter One and their experiences with the *Daily 5A's*. What were their reflections? Do they have any questions?

❑ Discuss Chapter Two: **Finances and Budgets**. Ask them to share how each of their respective families handles finances. Showing them the worksheet, describe how they can create a prospective budget as though they were married. There will be some items they won't know, so have them estimate about how much they think the various items will cost. Remind them to bring it with them for the next session.

❑ Prepare a sample budget to bring with you for illustration during your next meeting.

❑ Introduce them to Chapter Three: **Knowing Each Other**. Have each share his or her individual results from the **CORE Personality Inventory**; comparing scores, talking about similarities and differences. Be sure they focus on the positive traits, but begin to help them see that the weaknesses will eventually reveal themselves and probably become irritants. Therefore, they will need a plan in order to adjust to them. You can do part of the assignment with them and let them complete the rest of it on their own.

- ❑ Have them take the online **Love Language** test and bring the results with them to the next meeting. The test is found at: http://www.afo.net/hftw-lovetest.asp

- ❑ Introduce them to the **Similarities and Differences List** (pages 37-38). Because differences can create serious problems in marriage, have them discuss what adjustments might be needed. Ask them to put a **VS** next to the aspect they feel they are Very Similar, an **S** for those they are Similar, a **D** for those they are Different and an **ED** for those they are Extremely Different. Ask them to complete all assignments by the next meeting.

Session 3.

- ❑ Review their results from the online **Love Languages** test. Have them discuss specific things they can do to meet their partner's love language. Give them the assignment in the workbook for homework. If they didn't take the test online you can have them share their thoughts from the workbook questions.

- ❑ Go over their **Budget** with them. If they seem unrealistic in an area, be sure to discuss this in a way that is beneficial to them. Be careful not to use your example as the "correct" budgeted amounts. Let them know that budgets vary from couple to couple. Discuss all elements of home-ownership. Be sure to include taxes, insurance and interest as you discuss the budgeted amount for housing. Feel free to suggest that they take a trip around town and look at apartments or houses to determine a more accurate estimate of this expense. If their expenses are more than their income, facilitate discussion to resolve the problem. Remember not to give too much advice. They will learn more if they work out their differences or do the research to determine the realistic costs for items budgeted.

- ❑ Go over the **Similarities and Differences** (pages 37-38) with them. Ask them to share some of their thoughts with you; especially on areas they marked D (different) or ED (extremely different.) Share briefly how important it is to honestly discuss their **Similarities and Differences** in detail.

- ❑ Discuss the **Family of Origin** section (p. 39). Ask them to describe their upbringing. Ask them to do the assignment for next week. It would be best if you could share some experiences you have had regarding your own Family of Origin issues.

- ❑ Ask them to complete their Couples Assignments and Individual Reflection questions from each of the sections.

Session 4.

☐ Have them share their assignment from **Family of Origin**. Remind them that there is a tendency to become like our parents or the exact opposite. Ask them to describe what problems might occur from behaving or becoming the opposite of their parents.

☐ Introduce them to Chapter Four: **Resolving Conflicts and Managing Anger** (p. 43).

☐ **Statement to Diffuse Anger** (p. 43): Explain the process and ask them to decide on a statement they agree upon. You may use an example from your life or the example in the workbook.

☐ Teach the **Time-out Process** to them (pages 45-47). Share an example from your life, if you're willing.

☐ **8 Steps to Conflict Resolution** (p. 48): Ask them to think of a recurring conflict they have had or a current conflict with which they might be dealing. Show them the list of potential conflicts on page 51 and coach them through the 8 Steps. Be sure they do most of the talking.

☐ Give them the assignments from the above areas and ask them to continue doing their **Daily 5A's** and practice the **8 Steps to Conflict Resolution** if needed.

Session 5.

☐ Introduce them to Chapter Five: **A Biblical Perspective of Marriage**. Read the scriptures with them from **Biblical Partner** and ask them to complete their assignments for the next time you meet.

☐ **Leaving and Cleaving** (p. 57): This is often an area of conflict for couples, so have them discuss their thoughts and feelings regarding this issue. Again, use an example from your life or the example in the workbook.

☐ Briefly explain the **Responsibilities and Roles** (p. 60) material and ask them to do the assignment for the next session.

☐ Discuss the **Power of Encouragement** (p. 61) and the importance of positive affirmation. Ask them to share a few behaviors that they love about each other. Give them the assignment to be completed by the next session.

☐ Share the **Spirituality in Your Marriage** (p. 63) material with them. Discuss which spiritual disciplines you have found helpful in your life.

☐ Remind them to complete all their assignments and read Chapter Six: **Sexual Intimacy**.

Session 6.

❑ Begin this session by discussing any homework that hasn't been completed to this point.

❑ Discuss their **Responsibilities and Roles** assignment from the last session (p. 60).

❑ Have them share their **Spirituality in Your Marriage** assignment (p. 64).

❑ Introduce them to Chapter Six: **Sexual Intimacy**. Ask if their parents talked openly with them about sex. Walk them through the **Purity Agreement** (p. 72) and ask if they would consider making and signing this agreement.

❑ Share the **Prayer for Forgiveness** (p. 73) and invite them to pray it aloud while you lead them. Be sure not to force this on them or make them feel like they must do this now.

Session 7.

❑ Review Chapter Six: **Sexual Intimacy**. Ask if they have any questions.

❑ Introduce them to Chapter Seven: **Parenting**. Ask them to share their desires about beginning a family and the number of children they desire. Facilitate discussion about their parents' techniques and childrearing philosophies. (If they are blending a family, discuss the material on page 79 and have them share their expectations and concerns.)

❑ Discuss Chapter Eight: **Next Steps**: Allow plenty of time for them to discuss the **Red Flag** issues. Point out the resources from the Bibliography (pages 93-94) for future growth.

❑ Discuss the PREPARE/ENRICH Inventory (www.prepare-enrich.com); a certified trainer must facilitate results. If you are not trained in facilitating the **PREPARE/ENRICH Inventory**, help them find a pastor or counselor who is trained to review their results with them (more information is available at the website). If you are trained to facilitate the **PREPARE/ENRICH Inventory**, help the couple register for the Inventory and set up a final appointment with them to discuss their results. (Training is also available through our Newport Beach office.)

---

1 G. Rhoades, S. Stanley and H. Markman, *"The Pre-engagement Cohabitation Effect: A Replication and Extension of Previous Findings,"* Journal of Family Psychology 2009: 30 233.

2 Robert Oglesby, Personal interview, Director, Center for Youth and Family Ministry, Abilene Christian University, 242 Biblical Studies Building, Abilene, TX 79699.

3 Ted L. Huston, John P. Caughlin, Renate M. Houts, Shanna E. Smith, and Laura J. George, *"The Connubial Crucible: Newlywed Years as Predictors of Marital Delight, Distress and Divorce,"* The Journal of Personality and Social Psychology 2001 80: 237-252.

bibliography and additional resources

Allender, Dan, and Tremper Longman. <u>Intimate Allies</u>. Carol Stream, IL: Tyndale, 1995.

Benson, Harry. <u>Mentoring Marriages</u>. Grand Rapids, MI: Monarch Books, Kregel Publications, 2005.

Burkett, Larry. <u>The Complete Financial Guide for Young Couples</u>. Colorado Springs, CO: David C. Cook, 2005.

Chapman, Gary. <u>The Five Love Languages</u>. Chicago, IL: Northfield Publishing, 2004.

Deal, Ron. <u>The Smart Step Family</u>. Grand Rapids, MI: Bethany House Publishers, 2002.

Eggerichs, Emerson. <u>Love and Respect</u>. Brentwood, TN: Integrity Publishers, 2004.

Floyd, Scott. *"Newlyweds and Sex: What's Going on for Christian Couples?"* <u>Marriage and Family: A Christian Journal</u> Vol.7 Issue 1 (2004): 99-110.

Gottman, John. <u>The Seven Principles for Making Marriage Work</u>. New York, NY: Crown Publishing Group, 1999.

Gottman, John. <u>Why Marriages Succeed or Fail</u>. New York, NY: Fireside, 1994.

Gudgel, David. <u>Before You Live Together</u>. Ventura, CA: Regal Publishers, 2003.

Harley, Willard. <u>His Needs, Her Needs</u>. Grand Rapids, MI: Revell, 2001.

Harley, Willard. <u>Love Busters</u>. Grand Rapids, MI: Revell, 2002.

Hendrix, Howard and Helen Hunt. <u>Couplehood: The Imago Path to Real Love</u>. Croton Falls, NY: CASP, LLC, 2008.

Huston, Ted, and John Caughlin, R. Houts, S. Smith, and L. George. *"The Connubial Crucible: Newlywed Years as Predictors of Marital Delight, Distress and Divorce,"* <u>The Journal of Personality and Social Psychology</u> 80 (2001): 237-252.

Jayson, Sharon. *"Premarital Education Could Cut Divorce Rate,"* <u>USA Today</u>, June 22, 2006.

Laumann, Edward, John Gagnon, Robert Michael, and Stuart Michaels. <u>The Social Organization of Sexuality: Sexual Practices in the United States</u>. Chicago, IL: University of Chicago Press, 1994.

Lindau, Stacy, L. Schumm, E. Laumann, W. Levinson, Colin O'Muircheartaigh and L. Waite. *"A Study of Sexuality and Health among Older Adults in the United States,"* <u>New England Journal of Medicine</u> 8 (2007): 357-368.

Littauer, Florence and Marita Littauer. <u>Getting Along with Almost Anybody</u>. Grand Rapids, MI: Revell, 1998.

Luo, S., and E. Klohnen. *"Assortative Mating and Marital Quality in Newlyweds: A Couple-Centered Approach,"* <u>Journal of Personality and Social Psychology</u> University of Iowa (2005): Vol. 88 No 2. 304-326.

Markman, Howard, Scott Stanley, and Susan L. Blumberg. <u>Fighting For Your Marriage</u>. San Francisco, CA: Jossey-Bass Publishers, 1994.

Oglesby Robert, Director, <u>Study on Effect of Premarital Programs for Newlyweds</u>. Center for Youth and Family Ministry, Abilene Christian University, 242 Biblical Studies Building, Abilene, TX 79699

Olson, D., Olson-Sigg, A., and P. Larson. <u>The Couple Checkup</u>. Nashville, TN: Thomas Nelson, 2008.

Parrott, Les and Leslie. <u>The Complete Guide to Marriage Mentoring</u>. Grand Rapids, MI: Zondervan, 2005.

Penner, Clifford and Joyce. <u>Getting Your Sex Life Off to a Great Start.</u> Carol Stream, IL: W Publishing Group, 1994.

Penner, Clifford and Joyce. <u>Restoring The Pleasure</u>. Dallas, TX: Word Publishing, 1993.

Rhoades, G., Stanley S. and H. Markman. *"The Pre-engagement Cohabitation Effect: A Replication and Extension of Previous Findings,"* <u>Journal of Family Psychology</u> 30 (2009): 233-258.

Stanley, Scott, P. Amato, C. Johnson, and H. Markman. Premarital Education. <u>Journal of Family Psychology</u> (2006): Vol. 20 (1), 117-126.

Taylor, Gordon and Carrie. <u>Designing Successful Step Families</u>. Enumclaw, WA: Opportunities Unlimited 2003. www.designingdynamicstepfamilies.com

<u>The Couples' Devotional Bible</u>. Grand Rapids, MI: Zondervan Publishers, 2000.

Thomas, Gary. <u>Sacred Marriage</u>. Grand Rapids, MI: Zondervan Publishers, 2000.

Tirabassi, Roger and Becky. <u>Let Love Change Your Life Bible Study</u>. Newport Beach, CA: Becky Tirabassi Change Your Life®, Inc., 2000.

Watson D. Hubbard and D. Wiese. *"General Traits of Personality and Affectivity as Predictors of Satisfaction in Intimate Relationships: Evidence from Self-partner Ratings,"* <u>Journal of Personality</u> 3 (2001): 68.

Wright, Norman. <u>Couples Devotions for Engaged and Newlyweds</u>. Ventura CA: Regal Books, 1996.

Zenter, M.R., *"Mate Personality and Compatibility in Close Relationships: A Longitudinal Analysis,"* <u>Journal of Personality and Social Psychology</u> 89 (2005): 242-56.

Financial Tools

- Alcorn, Randy. <u>The Treasure Principle</u>. Sisters, Oregon, Multnomah Publisher, 2005.
- Crown Ministries   www.crown.org
- Burkett, Larry. <u>The Complete Financial Guide for Young Couples</u>. Colorado Springs, Co.: David C. Cook, 2005.
- Debt Free Living   Larry Burkett   www.cfcministry.org

Marriage Inventories

- Prepare/ Enrich   http://www.prepare-enrich.com

acknowledgments

This workbook is the culmination of years of work with premarital and married couples. It is the work of volunteers, marriage educators, pastors and counselors. I cannot begin to acknowledge the contributions of everyone who has ever influenced this work, but I especially want to thank my volunteers (Amy, Brian, Jen, Grant, Kristin, Michael, Dan, Denny and Sue) for the hours they have sacrificed to help prepare couples for marriage. I also want to thank Erin, Brenda and Reny for the help with the manuscript and production of this workbook.

I am especially grateful to **ROCK**HARBOR for allowing me to minister to *seriously dating and engaged couples* and encouraging me to complete this project. I must thank all of my mentors, Ashley, and the many volunteers who make the marriage ministry a priority in their lives.

I am most grateful for my wife, Becky. Without her assistance, I never would have completed this project. I want to especially thank her for her patience (just kidding,) love (not kidding,) her encouragement and amazing writing skills.

Last but not least, I want to thank each of you for taking the time to prepare yourselves for marriage. I believe this is the most important relationship of your life, second to your relationship with the Lord.

about the authors

Roger Tirabassi is a professional counselor, pastor, author, and seminar leader for singles, engaged, and married couples. He is devoted to equipping couples and individuals to reach their potential through thriving, healthy relationships with God and each other. Roger has a Master's degree in Pastoral Psychology and Counseling as well as a Doctorate of Ministry degree from Ashland Theological Seminary in Ashland, Ohio. In 1995, he founded Spiritual Growth Ministries, Inc., which presently serves pastors, couples, families and individuals through retreats, seminars and counseling. Roger is also a certified sports counselor and a Certified Director/Trainer of the PREPARE/ENRICH Inventory. Currently, Roger serves as the Pre-marital and Marriage Enrichment pastor at **ROCK**HARBOR Church in Costa Mesa, California.

Becky Tirabassi is the author of over fifteen books. She is a trained facilitator in the PREPARE/ENRICH Inventory, a certified Life Coach, an ACE Fitness Instructor, and a national speaker for organizations such as Women of Faith, Youth Specialties, and Women of Joy. She has appeared on numerous television shows such as the CBS Early Show, Fox and Friends, and ESPN's Cold Pizza. She is the president of *Becky Tirabassi Change Your Life®, Inc.* and founder of a student non-profit organization, Burning Hearts, Inc.

seriously dating or engaged.com

Check it out!

IF YOU WOULD LIKE TO...

- Purchase additional copies of Seriously Dating or Engaged: A Premarital Workbook or "Cool Tools" the pocket-sized edition of worksheets

- Receive quantity discounts for 10 or more Workbooks (includes a free copy for leader)

- Request information on an upcoming Seriously Dating or Engaged Seminar

- Schedule an event for your church or organization

Please visit, call, or write: Becky Tirabassi Change Your Life®, Inc.
Dr. Roger Tirabassi / rogertirabassi@gmail.com
Becky Tirabassi
Box 9672
Newport Beach, Ca. 92660
800-444-6189

www.changeyourlifedaily.com